Collins

Workbook

Delivering the

C000215903

NEW GCSE MATHS
Edexcel Linear
Matches the 2010 GCSE Specification

• Chris Pearce •

CONTENTS

Chapter 1: Number: Using a calculator   6

1.1 Arithmetic with a calculator   6
1.2 Fractions with a calculator   8
1.3 Calculator problems   11
PS   Making jewellery   16

Chapter 2: Geometry and measures: Constructions   18

2.1 Drawing triangles   18
2.2 Bearings   22
2.3 Maps and journeys   25
PS   Yacht race   28

Chapter 3: Number: Calculating with numbers   30

3.1 Multiplication and division   30
3.2 Rounding decimals   33
3.3 Working with decimals   35
3.4 Comparing fractions and decimals   38
3.5 Word expressions   40
FM   Eating out in France   44

Chapter 4: Statistics: Pie charts and surveys   46

4.1 Pie charts   46
4.2 Surveys   50
4.3 Using pie charts and questionnaires   53
FM   Where are all the people?   58

Chapter 5: Number: Percentages   60

5.1 Fractions, percentages and decimals   60
5.2 Calculation of percentages   63
5.3 Using percentages   67
FM   Examination marks   70

Chapter 6: Algebra: Using algebra   72

6.1 Writing expressions   72
6.2 Formulas   76
6.3 Using formulas   78
FM   Mobile phone deals   82

Chapter 7: Statistics: Averages   84

7.1 Averages and spread   84
7.2 The mean   88
7.3 Using statistics   91
PS   Goal!   96

Chapter 8: Geometry: Area and perimeter   98

8.1 Perimeter   98
8.2 Area   101
8.3 Using perimeter and area   105
FM   How big is a football pitch?   110

Chapter 9: Number: Ratio and proportion   112

9.1 Ratio   112
9.2 Speed   115
9.3 Using ratios in different contexts   118
FM   What's cooking?   122

Chapter 10:   Algebra: Equations   124

10.1   Missing numbers   124
10.2   Solving equations   127
10.3   Using equations   131
(FM)   The coach trip   134

**Chapter 11:   Algebra: Number
                sequences and patterns**   136

11.1   Sequences of numbers   136
11.2   Patterns and numbers   139
11.3   Patterns and numbers in action   142
(PS)   Is there anybody out there?   146

Chapter 12:   Geometry: Volume   148

12.1   Shapes made from cubes   148
12.2   Cuboids   151
12.3   Cuboids in real situations   155
(FM)   The juice of the orange   158

Chapter 13:   Geometry: Circles   160

13.1   Drawing circles   160
13.2   The circumference of a circle   164
13.3   Circles in action   167
(PS)   Television transmitters   170

Glossary   172
Answers at the back

INTRODUCTION

Welcome to Collins New GCSE Maths for Edexcel Linear Workbook 2.

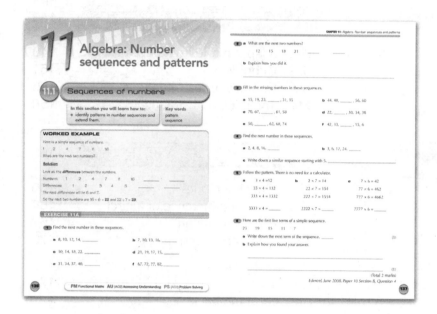

Worked examples

Understand the topic by reading the examples in blue boxes. These take you through questions step by step.

Colour-coded questions

Make progress as you move from red to orange to yellow questions.

Exam practice

Prepare for your exams with past exam questions.

Apply your maths

Practise maths questions in a range of situations in the separate section in yellow at the end of each chapter.

New Assessment Objectives

Check how well you have understood each topic with questions that assess your understanding marked (AU) and questions that test if you can solve problems marked (PS).

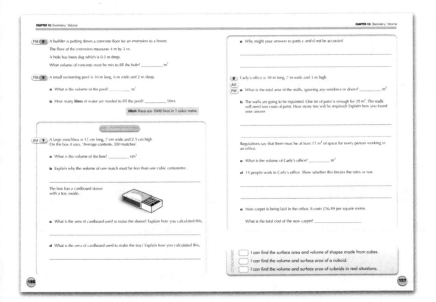

Checklist

Tick off the topics you can do on the checklist at the end of each chapter.

Helpful hints

Use hint boxes to give you tips as you work through the questions.

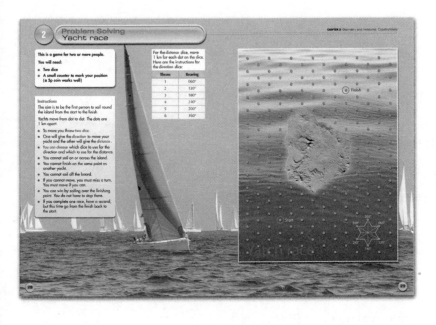

Functional maths

Practise functional maths skills to see how people use maths in everyday life. Look out for practice questions marked **FM** and there are also extra functional maths and problem-solving activities at the end of every chapter.

Answers

Check your own work with the answers at the back of the book.

Glossary

Look up unfamiliar words in the glossary at the back.

1

Number: Using a calculator

1.1 | Arithmetic with a calculator

In this section you will learn how to:
● use a calculator efficiently.

Key words
average
calculator
fraction

WORKED EXAMPLE

The ages of five people are 23, 28, 37, 41 and 46.

What is their average age?

Solution

To find the average, we add up the five ages and divide by 5.

We can do that with a calculator, using brackets like this:

$(23 + 28 + 37 + 41 + 44) \div 5 =$

On most calculators you also do it by pressing the keys shown here:

23 + 28 + 37 + 41 + 44 [=] [÷] 5 [=]

Check you can do it both ways on your calculator to get the answer 36.

EXERCISE 1A

Use a calculator to answer these questions.

1 Four elderly ladies said that their total age was 299 years.

Three of them were 82, 67 and 66.

How old was the fourth one?

2 Find half the sum of 654 and 978.

_____

3 Here are the temperatures on seven days in one week.

    14   17   16   19   18   11   10

What is the average for the week?

Hint: you must divide by 7.

_____

4 Ann has £185, Jean has £247 and Marie has £219.

They decide to put all their money together and share it out equally.

How much will each person get?

_____

FM 5 Yasmin is saving £15 a week from her salary.

How long will it take her to save £250?   _____

Explain how you know.

_____

AU 6 Work out the following:

$26 \times 26 - 27 \times 25 =$ _____

$43 \times 43 - 44 \times 42 =$ _____

$87 \times 87 - 88 \times 86 =$ _____

What do you notice?

_____

_____

Write another multiplication like the ones above.

_____

7 There are 60 minutes in an hour, 24 hours in a day and 365 days in a year.

a How many minutes are there in a day? _____

b How many hours are there in a year? _____

<hr>

Extension

PS **1** Two of the digits are missing in this multiplication.

Use a calculator to help you find them.

$\boxed{}6 \times \boxed{}4 = 1944$

PS **2** Find three different odd numbers, all larger than 5, which multiply to make 1001.

$\boxed{} \times \boxed{} \times \boxed{} = 1001$

AU **3** Carlos and Juan have 476 euros between them.

Carlos has 50 euros more than Juan.

How much does each one have?

_____

1.2 Fractions with a calculator

In this section you will learn how to:
● use a calculator to work with fractions.

Key words
fraction
mixed number

WORKED EXAMPLE

What is $\frac{3}{5} + \frac{7}{10}$?

Solution

Use your fraction button on your calculator.

It may give the answer as $\frac{13}{10}$ or as $1\frac{3}{10}$.

Make sure you know how to use your calculator with fractions.

EXERCISE 1B

1 Use the fraction key on your calculator to simplify these fractions.

a $\dfrac{8}{12} =$ _____

b $\dfrac{18}{24} =$ _____

c $\dfrac{18}{30} =$ _____

d $\dfrac{35}{40} =$ _____

2 Draw lines to join the equivalent fractions.

3 Find four fractions which are equivalent to $\dfrac{28}{40}$.

_____

_____

4 Add these fractions with a calculator.

a $\dfrac{1}{2} + \dfrac{1}{3} =$ _____

b $\dfrac{1}{4} + \dfrac{3}{8} =$ _____

c $\dfrac{1}{3} + \dfrac{1}{4} =$ _____

d $\dfrac{3}{4} + \dfrac{1}{8} =$ _____

e $\dfrac{1}{2} + \dfrac{1}{6} =$ _____

f $\dfrac{2}{3} + \dfrac{1}{6} =$ _____

PS 5 $\dfrac{1}{4} + \dfrac{1}{4} = \dfrac{1}{2}$

Can you find two **different** fractions which add up to $\frac{1}{2}$?

_____

> The fraction $\frac{7}{4}$ can be written as $1\frac{3}{4}$. The second way is called a **mixed number**. Make sure you can show this using a calculator.

6 Use a calculator to write these fractions as mixed numbers.

a $\frac{5}{4} =$ _____

b $\frac{7}{3} =$ _____

c $\frac{11}{4} =$ _____

d $\frac{23}{4} =$ _____

e $\frac{13}{3} =$ _____

f $\frac{17}{6} =$ _____

7 Add these fractions and give your answer as a mixed number. Use a calculator.

a $\frac{3}{4} + \frac{1}{2} =$ _____

b $\frac{1}{2} + \frac{2}{3} =$ _____

c $\frac{3}{4} + \frac{5}{8} =$ _____

d $\frac{7}{8} + \frac{1}{2} =$ _____

e $\frac{5}{8} + \frac{5}{8} =$ _____

f $\frac{7}{8} + \frac{7}{8} =$ _____

AU 8 **a** Explain how this clock face shows that $\frac{1}{4} + \frac{1}{3} + \frac{5}{12} = 1$.

_____

_____

b Check the addition is correct using your calculator.

9 Use your calculator to do these subtractions.

a $1 - \frac{1}{3} =$ _____

b $\frac{7}{8} - \frac{1}{4} =$ _____

c $1 - \frac{3}{4} =$ _____

d $\frac{5}{8} - \frac{1}{4} =$ _____

e $2 - \frac{3}{4} =$ _____

f $2 - \frac{2}{3} =$ _____

10 Fill in this addition table for fractions. Use a calculator to help you.

+	$\frac{1}{4}$	$\frac{1}{3}$	$\frac{1}{2}$	$\frac{3}{4}$
$\frac{1}{4}$				
$\frac{1}{3}$				
$\frac{1}{2}$				
$\frac{3}{4}$			$1\frac{1}{2}$	

(Extension)

(**AU** **1**) Calculate $\frac{3}{8} - \frac{1}{3} = $ _____.

How does this show that $\frac{3}{8}$ is bigger than $\frac{1}{3}$?

_____

(**AU** **2**) Which is bigger, $\frac{2}{3}$ of a cake or $\frac{5}{8}$ of a cake? Explain how you know.

_____

_____

(**3**) Use your calculator to find the following.

a $1\frac{1}{2} + 2\frac{3}{4} = $ _____   **b** $3\frac{1}{2} - 1\frac{3}{4} = $ _____   **c** $\frac{1}{2}$ of $5\frac{1}{2} = $ _____

1.3   Calculator problems

In this section you will learn how to:
● use a calculator to solve practical problems.

Key words
average
fraction

EXERCISE 1C

(**1**) This was the population of Margate in Kent at the time of the 2001 census.

Males	27 630
Females	30 835

a What was the total population of Margate? _____

b There were more females than males. How many more? _____

FM 2 Elise has four test marks on her college course.

They are 72, 49, 58 and 83.

To pass the course, she must have an average of at least 65. To find the average, she must add the marks and divide the answer by 4.

Has she passed? Give a reason for your answer.

_____

_____

PS 3 Here is a table of costs for hiring a car. The cost is in pounds per day.

Vehicle type	Up to 7 days	8 to 14 days	15 or more days
Compact	46	44	42
Intermediate	57	53	48
Station wagon	68	62	57

a Find the cost of a compact car for 13 days. _____

b Find the cost of a station wagon for 24 days. _____

c What is the difference in cost between a
station wagon and a compact car for a 9 day hire? _____

4 Here is part of Mrs Cook's gas bill.

Gas Bill

New reading   6549 units
Old reading   5137 units
_____

Cost per unit 25p

Work out the **total** cost of the units of gas she used.

£_____

(Total 3 marks)

Edexcel, November 2007, Paper 10 Section A Foundation, Question 9

PS 5 Here are the costs of a range of kitchen units.

Unit	Cost in pounds
Tall wall unit	56
Short wall unit	72
Cupboard unit	128
Drawer unit	156

Find the total cost of two tall wall units, two short wall units, three cupboard units and a drawer unit.

_____

FM 6 Andy and Becca want to buy some furniture. Here are some prices.

Furniture	Cost
Armchair	£795
Small sofa	£995
Medium sofa	£1145
Large sofa	£1275

They are thinking about two options.

A Two armchairs and a medium sofa.

B A large sofa and a small sofa.

Which option is cheaper and by how much?

_____

7 The cost of 30 litres of petrol is £28.80

Work out the cost of 1 litre of this petrol.

_____

(Total 3 marks)

Edexcel, November 2008, Paper 13 Foundation, Question 6

8 Complete this bill.

Michael's Cycle Repairs

Description	Number	Cost of each	Total
Brake blocks	4	£4.12	£16.48
Brake cables	2	£5.68	£_____
Pedals	2	£_____	£45.98
Labour charge $1\frac{1}{2}$ hours at £12.00 an hour			£_____
		Total	£_____

(Total 4 marks)

Edexcel, November 2008, Paper 13 Foundation, Question 8

Extension

1 You can use a calculator to find fractions of a quantity.

sale!
$\frac{1}{3}$ off all prices

For example, to find $\frac{2}{3}$ of £84 you calculate:

$$\frac{2}{3} \times 84 = 54$$

The answer is £54. This means that in a sale like the one advertised here, the sale price is $\frac{2}{3}$ of the original price.

Complete this table. The first item is done for you.

Item	Original price	Sale price
Camera	£84	£54
Headphones	£57	
Game console	£177	
Television	£468	

FM **2** The price of a computer is £396. The price in a sale is $\frac{1}{4}$ off if you buy it online, but there is a £45 delivery charge.

How much will it cost altogether to buy online?

_____

checklist

☐ I can use a calculator efficiently.

☐ I can use a calculator to work with fractions.

☐ I can use a calculator to solve practical problems.

Jewellery can be made from lengths of wire and beads.

Beads are sold in different sizes.

Wire is sold in different thicknesses, called the gauge.

To make a piece of jewellery the beads are threaded onto the wire.

Getting started

Step 1 Choose a gauge of wire and cut the length required.

Step 2 Put a fastener on one end.

Step 3 Thread beads of different sizes into a pattern.

Step 4 Put a fastener on the other end. Your jewellery is now complete.

Hint: for bracelets and anklets use 20-gauge wire. For necklaces use 24-gauge wire.

Beads are available in three lengths:
- 6 mm
- 8 mm
- 10 mm

Beads are available in four colours:
- green
- blue
- red
- yellow

Task A

1 How many 6 mm beads are needed to make a bracelet?

2 How many 8 mm beads are needed to make an anklet?

3 How many 10 mm beads are needed to make a short necklace?

4 How many 10 mm beads are needed to make a long necklace?

Task B

You are asked to make a bracelet with beads of two different lengths.

You decide to use 6 mm red beads and 8 mm blue beads.

How many would you need if you used them alternately?

Standard lengths for bracelets and necklaces	
Bracelet	17 cm
Anklet	23 cm
Short necklace	39 cm
Long necklace	46 cm
Remember 1 cm = 10 mm	

Task C

Design a piece of jewellery of your choice.

Make a list of all the materials you need. Specify the number of beads and length of wire.

Task D

Work out the cost of your design.

Use the information in the table below.

Price	
6 mm beads	10p each
8 mm beads	12p each
10 mm beads	15p each
24-gauge wire	10p per cm
20-gauge wire	8p per cm
Fasteners for both ends	30p per item of jewellery

2 Geometry and measures: Constructions

Drawing triangles

In this section you will learn how to:
● draw triangles accurately using given measurements.

Key words
angle
triangle

WORKED EXAMPLE

Draw this triangle accurately.

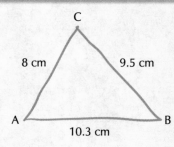

Solution

Start by drawing the line from A to B 10.3 cm long.

Next, open your compasses to 8 cm.

Put the point on A and draw an arc.
This is drawn to a smaller scale here.

You will need a ruler and a pair of compasses.

Now open the compasses to 9.5 cm.

Put the point on B and draw a second arc.

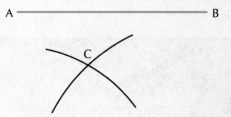

FM Functional Maths **AU** (AO2) Assessing Understanding **PS** (AO3) Problem Solving

Where the arcs cross is point C.

Draw in the other two sides.

Check the sides by measuring them.

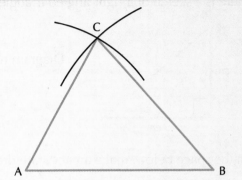

EXERCISE 2A

1 Measure the lengths of these lines in centimetres.

a _____

Length = _____ cm

b _____

Length = _____ cm

c _____

Length = _____ cm

2 Measure the lengths of these lines and the angle between them. Label these on the diagram below.

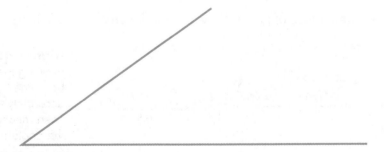

3 Here is a sketch of a right-angled triangle.

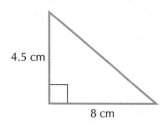

Diagram not accurately drawn

In the space below, make an accurate drawing of this triangle.

(Total 3 marks)

Edexcel, November 2009, Paper 11, Question 9

Extension

1 Draw these triangles accurately on a separate piece of paper. Use a ruler and a protractor. In each case measure the third **side in your drawing**. The triangles below are not drawn accurately.

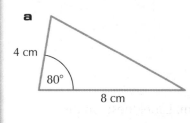

a _____ cm

b _____ cm

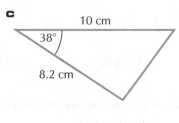

c _____ cm

2 Draw these triangles on a separate piece of paper. They are not drawn accurately here.

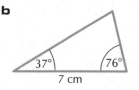

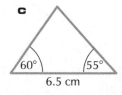

Hint: start by drawing the base line accurately. Then measure the angle and draw a line at each end.

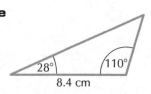

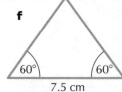

3 Look at the triangles in question 2.

    a What type of triangle is **d**? _____

    b Measure the other two sides on your drawing of triangle **d**. They should be the same length.

    c What type of triangle is **f**? _____

    d How long should the other sides of triangle **f** be? _____

    e Measure the sides of triangle **f** to check your accuracy.

You will need a pair of compasses for these questions.

4 Draw these triangles accurately on a separate piece of paper.

    Hint: use the method shown in the example.

a

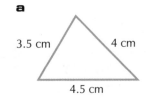

b

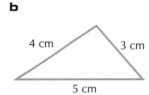

5 If you have drawn triangle **b** in question 4 accurately, one of the angles should be a right angle.
Measure it to check your accuracy.

AU 6 **a** Draw this triangle accurately on a separate piece of paper.

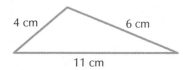

    b Explain what happens.

_____

_____

    c Make your own sketch of an impossible triangle.

2.2 Bearings

In this section you will learn how to:
● use a bearing to describe a direction.

Key words
angle
bearing
clockwise
direction

WORKED EXAMPLE

The scale of a map is 1 cm to 20 km.

Freshton is 90 km from Walden at a bearing of 260 degrees.

Mark it on the map.

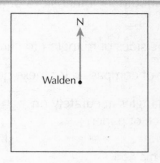

Solution

Draw a line from Walden. The bearing is the angle clockwise from north.

It is over half a complete turn because it is more that 180 degrees.

260 − 180 = 80 so we need to measure 180 + 80 degrees.

Use a protractor.

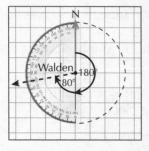

The distance is 90 km. On the map that is 90 ÷ 20 = 4.5 cm.

Measure 4.5 cm from Walden to find Freshton.

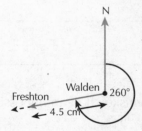

EXERCISE 2B

1 Find the bearing from Aybury of these towns.

Bearings are written with three digits so the bearing of Besley from Aybury is 050°.

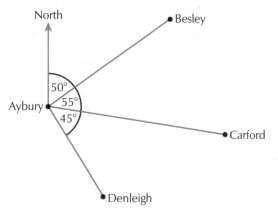

a Carford _____

b Denleigh _____

> **Hint:** the drawings are not accurate. You cannot use a protractor.

2 Find the bearing of the other landmarks from the station.

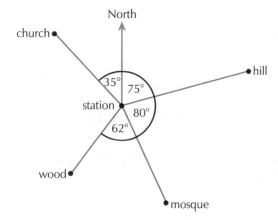

hill: _____ °

mosque: _____ °

wood: _____ °

church: _____ °

3 **a** Find the bearing of Eastley from Weston. _____ °

b Find the bearing of Weston from Eastley. _____ °

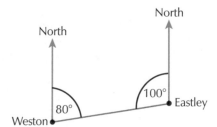

Extension

1 The diagram shows the position of two airports, *A* and *B*.

A plane flies from airport *A* to airport *B*.

Scale: 1 cm represents 50 km

a Measure the size of the angle marked *x*.

_____ °   (1)

b Work out the real distance between airport *A* and airport *B*.
Use the scale 1 cm represents 50 km.

_____ km   (2)

(Total 3 marks)

Edexcel, May 2008, Paper 12, Question 13 a and b

2 The scale of this map is 1 cm to 5 miles.

a Measure the distance from Castorleigh to Farnbury.

_____ miles

b Find the bearing from Castorleigh to Farnbury.

_____ °

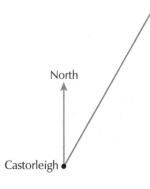

c The bearing from Castorleigh to Walbridge is 110°. Draw a line in this direction on the map.

d The distance from Castorleigh to Walbridge is 40 miles. Mark Walbridge on the map.

2.3 Maps and journeys

In this section you will learn how to:
● use bearings in realistic situations.

Key words
angle
bearing
direction

EXERCISE 2C

PS **1** Bearings are used by planes and ships to specify the direction to travel.

Write down the bearings of each of these compass directions.

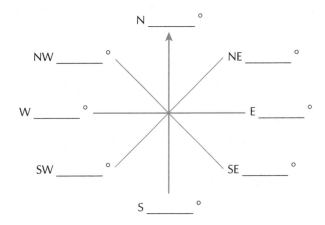

2 This map shows three airports in France and Spain.

On the map, mark angles to show these bearings.

a The bearing of Bordeaux from Madrid is 030°.

b The bearing of Barcelona from Bordeaux is 152°.

c The bearing of Madrid from Barcelona is 257°.

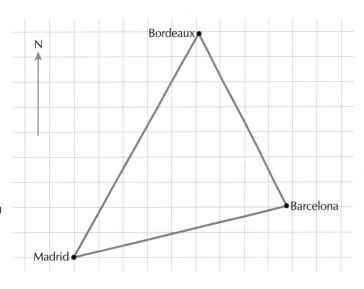

3 This map shows two islands in the Mediterranean Sea.

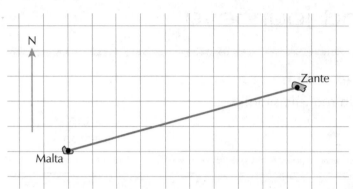

You are taking a boat from Malta to Zante.

Hint: draw a north line from Malta to help you measure the angle.

a On what bearing will you travel? _____ °

b The scale of the map is 1 cm to 100 km. How far apart are the islands?

_____

c If you travel from Zante back to Malta, what is the bearing for this journey? _____ °

FM 4 This chart shows two stages of an aircraft's flight from Glasgow to Manchester.

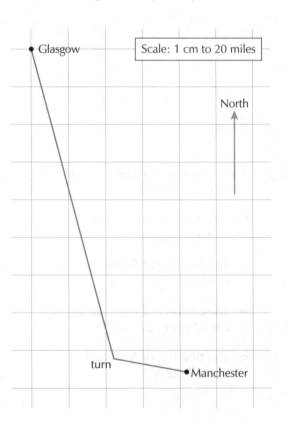

a Describe the distance and bearing for each stage of the journey.

Put your answers in this table.

	Bearing	**Distance**
Glasgow to turn		
turn to Manchester		

Hint: draw north lines at Glasgow and at the turn.

b Why do you think the plane did not fly directly to Manchester?

_____

_____

Extension

1 Here is Birmingham airport marked on a map. The scale of the map is 1 cm to 20 miles.

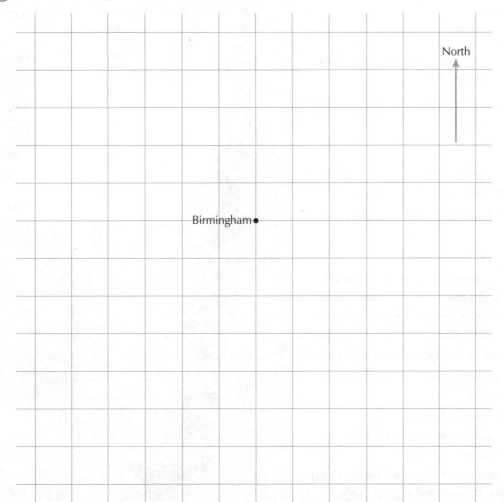

This table shows the distance and bearings of some other airports from Birmingham. Show the airports on the map.

Compare your finished map with your neighbour's.

Airport	Bearing from Birmingham	Distance from Birmingham
Gatwick	145°	116 miles
Leeds-Bradford	010°	94 miles
Southampton	168°	106 miles
Cardiff	225°	90 miles
Liverpool	327°	84 miles

checklist

☐ I can draw triangles accurately using given measurements.

☐ I can use a bearing to describe a direction.

☐ I can use bearings in realistic situations.

This is a game for two or more people.

You will need:

- **Two dice**
- **A small counter to mark your position (a 5p coin works well)**

Instructions

The aim is to be the first person to sail round the island from the start to the finish.

Yachts move from dot to dot. The dots are 1 km apart.

- To move you throw **two dice**.
- One will give the **direction** to move your yacht and the other will give the **distance**.
- **You can choose** which dice to use for the direction and which to use for the distance.
- You cannot sail on or across the island.
- You cannot finish on the same point as another yacht.
- You cannot sail off the board.
- If you cannot move, you must miss a turn. You must move if you can.
- You can win by sailing over the finishing point. You do not have to stop there.
- If you complete one race, have a second, but this time go from the finish back to the start.

For the **distance** dice, move 1 km for each dot on the dice. Here are the instructions for the **direction** dice:

Throw	Bearing
1	060°
2	120°
3	180°
4	240°
5	300°
6	360°

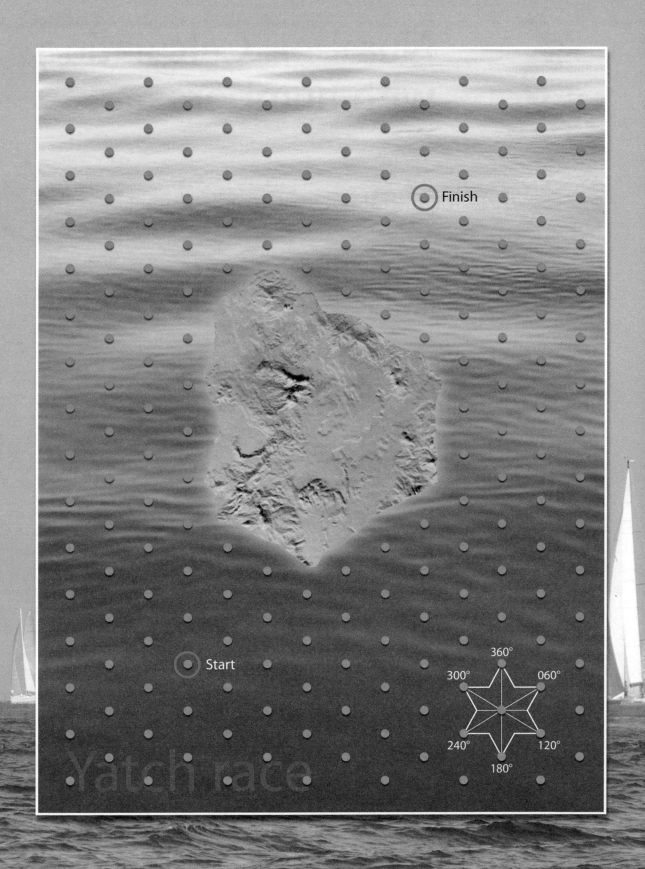

Number: Calculating with numbers

3.1 Multiplication and division

In this section you will learn how to:
- multiply and divide by a 2 digit number without a calculator.

Key words
divide
multiply

WORKED EXAMPLE

1 Find 32×46 without using a calculator.

Solution

You could use a grid method:

×	30	2
40	1200	80
6	180	12

$1200 + 80 = 1280$

$180 + 12 = 192$

Answer $= 1280 + 192 = 1472$

Or you could use a column method:

$$\begin{array}{r} 32 \\ \times \; 46 \\ \hline 192 \\ 1280 \\ \hline 1472 \end{array}$$

192 — 32 multiplied by 6

1280 — 32 multiplied by 4
Note: write down 0 first, then multiply by 4.

Use the method you prefer.

2 Find $782 \div 23$ without a calculator.

Solution

$$\begin{array}{r} 34 \\ 23\overline{)782} \\ -\;69\downarrow \\ \hline 92 \\ 92 \\ \hline 0 \end{array}$$

So $782 \div 23 = 34$

Start with 'How many 23s in 7? There are none, of course, so move on to 78.

Look at the 23 times table to find the biggest number which is less than 78. This is 69, which is 3 × 23. Put 3 on the top line.

Take away 69 from 78 and bring down the 2.

Look again at the 23 times table to find that 4 × 23 = 92. Now put 4 on the top line.

Because 92 taken away from 92 leaves 0, you have finished.

EXERCISE 3A

Do not use a calculator in this exercise.

1 Do these multiplications. The first has been done for you.

a $20 \times 30 = 600$

b $20 \times 40 = $ _____

c $30 \times 50 = $ _____

d $60 \times 40 = $ _____

2 $63 \times 70 = 4410$ Use this to help you write down the answers to these.

a $63 \times 7 = $ _____

b $630 \times 70 = $ _____

3 Complete this multiplication table.

×	7	70	700	7000
6			4200	

4 Fill in the missing numbers in this multiplication table.

×	4	40
7		
70		

5 Work out these multiplications.

		Calculations	Answer
a	23×12		
b	72×14		
c	41×28		
d	57×25		

6 27 × 53 = 1431 Use this to write down the answers to these.

a 53 × 27 = _____ **b** 1431 ÷ 27 = _____ **c** 1431 ÷ 53 = _____

7 87 × 73 = 6351

Use this to write down two different divisions.

_____ and _____

8 Work out these divisions without using a calculator.

		Calculations	Answer
a	96 ÷ 8		
b	156 ÷ 12		
c	672 ÷ 21		
d	700 ÷ 25		

Extension

AU 1 Which is larger: 47 × 63 or 43 × 67 ? What is the difference between them?

_____

_____

2 2016 ÷ ★ = 63

What number does ★ represent?

_____

3.2 Rounding decimals

In this section you will learn how to:
● round decimals to a number of decimal places.

Key words
decimal place
rounding
whole number

WORKED EXAMPLE

Share £620 equally between 13 people.

<u>Solution</u>

We need to do a division. ————→ Share means divide.

With a calculator, 620 ÷ 13 = 47.692307…

We need to round this off sensibly.

To the nearest pound it is £48. ————→ We round up because the first digit after the decimal point is 6.

To the nearest penny it is £47.69. ————→ We do <u>not</u> round up because the third digit after the decimal point is only 2.

Either of these is a sensible answer.

Could you actually give everyone £48?

No, because 13 × 48 is more than £620.

EXERCISE 3B

1 Round off each of these numbers to the nearest whole number.

a 42.7 _____   b 51.9 _____   c 2.4 _____

d 3.5 _____   e 11.8 _____   f 15.1 _____

g 3.23 _____   h 81.22 _____   i 98.61 _____

j 66.53 _____   k 13.45 _____   l 8.99 _____

2 Put a circle around the correct answer. Each number must be rounded to 1 decimal place. The first one has been done for you.

a 5.24   (5.2)   or   5.3   b 6.75   6.7   or   6.8

c 8.88   8.8   or   8.9   **d** 14.53   14.5   or   14.6

e 11.621   11.6   or   11.7   **f** 58.452   58.4   or   58.5

g 8.554   8.5   or   8.6   **h** 3.751   3.7   or   3.8

3 Round off the following numbers to 2 decimal places.

a 4.657 _____   **b** 3.342 _____   **c** 8.875 _____

d 11.319 _____   **e** 32.897 _____   **f** 14.3246 _____

4 If 7 people share £200 equally, how much will each one get?

_____

Hint: use a calculator. Round off your answer to the nearest penny.

5 Here are some calculator answers. Round them off to 1 decimal place.

	Division	Calculator answer	Rounded to 1 decimal place
a	53 ÷ 7	7.57142….	
b	183 ÷ 11	16.63636….	
c	222 ÷ 17	13.05882….	
d	1000 ÷ 21	47.61904….	

6 Use a calculator to find $\frac{1}{7}$ of 20. Round off your answer to 2 decimal places. _____

Hint: find $\frac{1}{7}$ by dividing by 7.

Extension

AU 1 Work with a partner on this question.

13 people want to share £200 as equally as possible. What is the best way to do this? Will there be any money left over?

_____

3.3 Working with decimals

In this section you will learn how to:
● complete calculations using decimal numbers.

Key words
add
decimal
divide
multiply
subtract

WORKED EXAMPLE

What is the difference between 3.7 × 5 and 5.7 × 3?

<u>Solution</u>

First do the two multiplications.

3.7 × 5 = 18.5

5.7 × 3 = 17.1 ——————→ Check these are correct.

Now do the subtraction.

18.5 − 17.1 = 1.4 ——————→ Remember, 'difference' means subtract.

EXERCISE 3C

Do not use a calculator in this exercise.

1 Do these additions and subtractions.

		Calculations	Answer
a	2.49 + 3.25		
b	3.7 + 5.8 + 4.1		
c	12.3 − 8.6		

		Calculations	Answer
d	10 − 6.3		

2 Do these multiplications.

		Calculations	Answer
a	2.7 × 3		
b	3.61 × 4		
c	5 × 2.8		
d	12.6 × 6		

3 Do these divisions.

		Calculations	Answer
a	5.7 ÷ 3		
b	5.44 ÷ 4		
c	2.65 ÷ 5		
d	22.32 ÷ 6		

4 If one pack of dog food cost £2.40, what will four cost?

_____

5 If a pack of five pairs of socks costs £9.50, what is the cost of one pair?

_____

Extension

1 Julie buys four frozen pizzas for £3.20 each and three litres of milk for £1.15 each. How much change will she have from a £20 note?

_____

2 $27 \times 35 = 945$

Use this to write down the answers to the following multiplications.

Use a calculator to check that you are correct.

a $27 \times 3.5 =$ _____   **b** $2.7 \times 35 =$ _____   **c** $0.27 \times 35 =$ _____

3 $18 \times 6.3 = 113.4$

Use this to write down the answers to the following multiplications.

Use a calculator to check that you are correct.

a $18 \times 63 =$ _____   **b** $1.8 \times 63 =$ _____

4 $37 \times 1.8 = 66.6$

Use this to write down the answers to the divisions.

Use a calculator to check that you are correct.

a $66.6 \div 1.8 =$ _____   **b** $66.6 \div 18 =$ _____

3.4 Comparing fractions and decimals

In this section you will learn how to:
● recognise when simple fractions and decimals are the same.

Key words
decimal
fraction

WORKED EXAMPLE

Write $\frac{3}{8}$ and $\frac{1}{3}$ as a decimal.

You can use a calculator to do this.

Solution

$3 \div 8 = 0.375$

$1 \div 3 = 0.3333...$

You could round this off to two decimal places. $\frac{1}{3} = 0.33$

Hint: You should learn these.

$\frac{1}{2} = 0.5$ $\qquad$ $\frac{1}{4} = 0.25$ $\qquad$ $\frac{1}{10} = 0.1$

EXERCISE 3D

1 Write these fractions as decimals. You should not need a calculator.

a $\frac{3}{4} =$ _____ **b** $\frac{3}{10} =$ _____ **c** $\frac{7}{10} =$ _____ **d** $\frac{1}{5} =$ _____

Hint: $\frac{3}{4} = \frac{1}{2} + \frac{1}{4}$.

Hint: $\frac{1}{5} = \frac{2}{10}$.

2 Use a calculator to write these fractions as decimals.

a $\frac{1}{8} =$ _____ **b** $\frac{5}{8} =$ _____ **c** $\frac{7}{8} =$ _____ **d** $\frac{13}{20} =$ _____

3 Use a calculator to write $\frac{2}{3}$ as a decimal.

_____

4 Use the fact that $\frac{1}{5} = 0.2$ to write these fractions as decimals.

a $\frac{2}{5} = $ _____ b $\frac{3}{5} = $ _____ c $\frac{4}{5} = $ _____

Hint: $\frac{2}{5}$ is double $\frac{1}{5}$.

AU 5 a Which is larger, $\frac{3}{4}$ or 0.8 ? Give a reason for your answer.

Answer: _____

Reason: _____

b Which is the smallest: $\frac{1}{3}$ or 0.35? Give a reason for your answer.

Answer: _____

Reason: _____

Extension

AU 1 This answer to the question 'Which is larger, $\frac{5}{8}$ or 0.72?' is <u>incorrect</u>:

$\frac{5}{8} = 5 \div 8 = 0.625$

625 is larger than 72, so $\frac{5}{8}$ is larger than 0.72.

What is the mistake? How would you correct it?

_____

_____

3.5 Word questions

In this section you will learn how to:
- be able to answer questions involving decimals in real-life contexts.

Key words
per hour
total

EXERCISE 3E

You may use a calculator in this exercise if you wish.

> **Gift shop**
>
> *Price list*
>
> | | |
> |---|---|
> | Key ring | £3.20 |
> | Hat | £3.99 |
> | Pencil case | £2.70 |
> | Ruler | 45p |
> | Pen | 60p |
> | Pencil | |

Keith buys 3 pens.

a Work out the total cost.   £_____   (2)

Simon buys a pencil case, a ruler and a pen.

He pays with a £5 note.

b Work out how much change he should get.   £_____   (3)

The gift shop also sells pencils.

The price of a pencil is $\frac{2}{3}$ the price of a pen.

c Work out the price of a pencil.   _____p   (2)

(Total 7 marks)

Edexcel, November 2008, Paper 1 Foundation, Question 9

2 Here are the prices for prints from a digital camera at a photo shop.
They are available in three sizes.

Small	Medium	Large
15p per print	25p per print	32p per print

Find these costs in pounds.

a 30 small prints £ _____

b 20 medium prints £ _____

c 10 large prints and 40 small prints

£ _____

3 Tareq buys two books. One costs £6.99 and the other costs £8.99.

a What is the total cost? _____

b How much change will Tareq have from £20? _____

PS **4** New classroom chairs cost £14.49 each.

a How many can you buy for £100? _____

b How much would it cost to buy a set of 35? _____

5 Josh buys 40 litres of milk.

The total cost is £33.20

Work out the cost of 1 litre of the milk. _____ (3)

(Total 3 marks)

Edexcel, June 2008, Paper 13 Foundation, Question 4

FM 6 The road tax for a car depends on the model.
You can pay for 12 months or 6 months.
Artem checks the rate for his car.
The 12 months rate is £175; the 6 months rate is £96.25.
How much <u>extra</u> will he pay **in a year** if he chooses the 6 months rate?

_____

FM 7 Here are the admission costs
at a theme park.

Adult	£29.50
Child	£22.50
Family of 3	£66.00
Family of 4	£83.00
Family of 5	£101.00
Family of 6	£119.10

a Nathan visits the park with his mother and
father. How much will they save by buying a
family ticket?

_____

b How much would a family of two adults and
four children save by buying a family ticket?

_____

PS 8 a Lucas is paid £7.75 an hour and works a 32 hour week.
How much does he earn in a week?

_____

b Lucas's sister earns £291.20 for a 32 hour week.
How much is she paid per hour?

_____

Extension

Hint: you must add the four sides of the rectangle.

1 The sides of a rectangular room are 3.65 metres and 6.25 metres.

What is the perimeter of the room? _____

FM 2 Ella is looking at mobile phone contracts.
Here are two possible deals.

Mobilz	Uconnect
● Initial payment £25.50	● No initial payment
● Pay £8.45 a month for 18 months	● Pay £10.75 a month for 18 months

Which do you think is better value? Give a reason for your answer.

When you have your answer, see if other people have come to the same conclusion.

The better value is: _____

Reason: _____

_____

_____

checklist

☐ I can multiply and divide by a 2 digit number without a calculator.

☐ I can round decimals to a number of decimal places.

☐ I can complete calculations using decimal numbers.

☐ I can recognise when simple fractions and decimals are the same.

☐ I can answer questions involving decimals in realistic contexts.

Angie and Ken were on holiday in France.

They went to a restaurant.

Here is the menu. All prices are in euros.

Entrées

Mousse de saumon et câpres Salmon mousse with capers	€5.50
Soupe à l'oignon au gratin Onion soup	€4.70
Salade aux noix et au roquefort Salad with walnuts and Roquefort	€4.60

Plats principaux

Escalope de veau Veal escalope	€10.50
Gigot d'agneau braisé Braised lamb	€13.20
Rôti de boeuf Roast beef	€14.25
Filet mignon aux oignons avec un gratin dauphinois Pork fillet with onions and dauphinoise oven baked potatoes	€15.30

Desserts

Salade de fruits frais Fresh fruit salad	€4.25
Profiteroles au chocolat Chocolate profiteroles	€4.75
Crème brûlée	€6.25

Task A

1 What are the costs of the cheapest and most expensive three-course meals?

Here is what Angie and Ken ordered.

Angie: soup, roast beef and fruit salad.

Ken: salad, lamb and profiteroles.

2 Find the cost of Angie's meal and Ken's meal.

Angie had two mineral waters that cost €1.75 each.

Ken had an orange juice that cost €2.20.

3 What is the total cost of Angie and Ken's meal, including drinks?

They decided to leave a 10% tip for the waiter.

4 What is 10% of the total cost of their meal?

> **Hint:** 10% is the same as $\frac{1}{10}$.
> To find it, divide by 10.

5 How much did they pay including the tip?

They want to know how much they paid in pounds. The exchange rate was €1 = £0.91.

6 Convert the total amount of their bill, including the tip, into pounds.

Task B

Choose a meal of your own and find the cost in pounds.

Soft drinks, if you want one, are the same price as the orange juice.

Do not forget to leave a 10% tip.

Statistics: Pie charts and surveys

4.1 Pie charts

In this section you will learn how to:
- interpret and draw pie charts.

Key words
frequency
pie chart

WORKED EXAMPLE

Calculate the angles needed to draw a pie chart.

Clothes size	Number of people
S	20
M	35
L	40
XL	25

Solution

First find the number of people in the survey.
20 + 35 + 40 + 25 = 120

There are 360 degrees at the centre of the pie chart.

Each person has 360 ÷ 120 = 3°.

Multiply the number of people in each group by 3 to find the angle.

Clothes size	Number of people	Angle in pie chart	
S	20	60°	→ 20 × 3 = 60
M	35	105°	→ 35 × 3 = 105
L	40	120°	→ 40 × 3 = 120
XL	25	75°	→ 25 × 3 = 75
Total	120	360°	

The pie chart can now be drawn.

EXERCISE 4A

1 40 students voted for the colour of a new uniform. The results are shown in this pie chart.

How many voted for each colour?

Blue _____   Red _____

Green _____   Purple _____

Hint: remember, there are 40 students altogether.

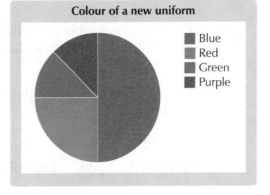

Colour of a new uniform

- Blue
- Red
- Green
- Purple

2 A survey of where the employees of a firm lived had these results.

Location	City	Town	Village	Country
Percentage	20%	40%	30%	10%

Show the results on this pie chart. Remember to label each section.

Hint: the points on the circle show 10% intervals.

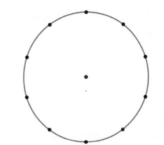

3 Here are the results of a survey of the large trees in a park.

There were 36 trees altogether.

Because $360 \div 36 = 10$, there will be 10 degrees at the centre for each tree.

Measure the angles at the centre of each sector. Work out the number of trees. The first one has been done for you.

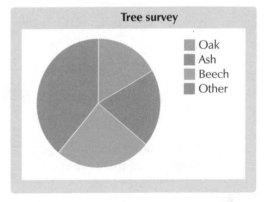

Tree survey

- Oak
- Ash
- Beech
- Other

Oak: Angle = 60°   Number of trees = 6   That is 60 ÷ 10

Ash: Angle = _____°   Number of trees = _____

Beech: Angle = _____°   Number of trees = _____

Other: Angle = _____°   Number of trees = _____

Hint: check that the total number of trees is 36.

4 Jasmine carried out a survey of favourite football teams. She asked 30 people. Here are the results.

She wants to draw a pie chart. She must work out the angle of each sector. She has asked for your help.

Complete this calculation to find the angle for each voter.

$$360 \div 30 = \text{_____}$$

Now fill in the Angles column of the table.

Team	Votes	Angle of pie chart
Rovers	9	
City	10	
United	4	
Town	7	
Total	30	360°

Hint: the Rovers' angle will be 9 × the angle for each person.

5 Colin carried out a survey. He asked some students in Year 10 which type of film they liked best. He used the results to draw this pie chart.

a What fraction of the students said 'Comedy'?

_____ (1)

b 20 said 'Horror'. Work out the total number of students Colin asked.

_____ (2)

(Total 3 marks)

Edexcel, March 2009, Paper 5 Foundation, Question 3

Extension

1 On a separate piece of paper, draw a pie chart to show the results of Jasmine's survey in question 4 of this section.

AU 2 Work with a partner on this question.

A shop carried out a survey of the gender of adult visitors one Saturday. They recorded morning and afternoon separately.

The results are shown in these pie charts.

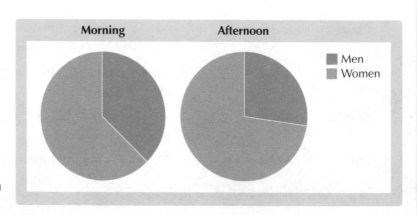

For each of the following statements write 'True', 'False' or 'Cannot tell'.

a There were more women than men in the morning. _____

b There were more women in the morning than in the afternoon. _____

c There were more customers in the afternoon than in the morning. _____

d There were more men than women in the afternoon. _____

e There was a smaller proportion of men in the afternoon than in the morning.

_____

f Over half the shoppers were men. _____

g The number of customers in the morning and in the afternoon was the same.

_____

h Women enjoy shopping more than men. _____

i There were more shoppers on Saturday than there were on Friday. _____

See whether other students have the same answers as you to this question.

PS 3 60 students were asked to choose one of four subjects.

The table gives information about their choices.

Subject	Number of students	Angle
Art	12	72°
French	10	
History	20	
Music	18	

Complete the pie chart to show this information.

(Total 3 marks)

Edexcel, November 2008 Paper 5/8, Question 4

4.2 Surveys

In this section you will learn how to:
- criticise questionnaires.

Key words

biased

survey

WORKED EXAMPLE

Here is a survey question.

How many days were you absent from school last term?

1 to 5 ☐   5 to 10 ☐   10 or more ☐

What things are wrong with this question?

Solution

There are several things that need to be changed:

1   There is no box for 0 days.

2   If you were absent for 5 days you could tick the first or the second box.

3   If you were absent for 10 days you could tick the second or third box.

4   You might find it hard to remember the whole of last term.

You could change the boxes like this:

None ☐   1 to 5 ☐   6 to 10 ☐   11 or more ☐

There still might be a problem if someone was absent for half a day.

So this could be another way:

5 or less ☐   More than 5 but not more than 10 ☐   More than 10 ☐

EXERCISE 4B

Work with a partner on this exercise.

1 Here is a question in a survey.

How did you come to school today?
Tick one box

walk ☐   cycle ☐   car ☐

   a The boxes do not include all the possibilities. What other options could be included?

   _____

   b Why is it a good idea to include a box for 'other'?

   _____

   c If the question were changed to 'How do you come to school?', why might some students find it difficult to fill in one box?

   _____

   _____

2 Here is a survey question.

Why is it a good idea to give school students a lot of homework?
Tick at least one box.

☐ It will help them learn more.

☐ It will keep them off the streets.

☐ It will stop them playing computer games.

   a Why is this a biased question? _____

   b What would be a fairer question to ask? _____

   _____

3 Poppy wants to find out for how much time people use their computer.

She uses this question on a questionnaire:

> For how much time do you use your computer?
>
> 0–1 hours ☐   3–4 hours ☐
>
> 1–2 hours ☐   4–5 hours ☐
>
> 2–3 hours ☐   5–6 hours ☐

Write down **two** things that are wrong with this question.

1 _____

2 _____

(Total 2 marks)

Edexcel, November 2008, Paper 5/8 Foundation, Question 6

4 James wants to find out how many text messages people send.

He uses this question on a questionnaire:

> "How many text messages do you send?"
>
> ☐   ☐   ☐   ☐
>
> 1–10   11–20   21–30   more than 30

a Write down **two** things wrong with this question.

1 _____

2 _____ (2)

b James asks 10 students in his class to complete his questionnaire.

Give **one** reason why this may not be a suitable sample.

_____ (1)

(Total 3 marks)

Edexcel, March 2009, Paper 5 Foundation, Question 4

┌─────────────────────────────┐
│   Extension   │
└─────────────────────────────┘

1 A school wants to try to gain a Healthy Eating Award.

Jake has been asked to carry out a survey of what students eat for lunch.

He decides to ask all the boys in his class.

a Give two reasons why this would not be a representative sample of the all the students in the school.

Reason 1 _____

Reason 2 _____

b Suggest how he could improve his survey.

_____

_____

4.3

Using pie charts and questionnaires

In this section you will learn how to:
- interpret pie charts and questionnaires in real situations.

Key words

pie chart
questionnaire
survey

WORKED EXAMPLE

Carlotta writes for her school magazine.

She wants to write an article about who will win an election for a new student representative on the school council.

She has carried out a survey of who students say they will vote for.

a Give three reasons why a pie chart is a good way to show this information.

b Give one disadvantage of a pie chart.

Solution

a Here are three advantages:

   i You can see which candidate will probably get the largest vote.

   ii You can see what fraction of the vote each person will probably get, which is hard to see in a bar chart.

   iii If someone else does a pie chart of a similar survey, it will be easy to compare the two. It will not matter if there are different numbers of people in the two surveys.

b A disadvantage is that you cannot tell how many students took part in the survey.

EXERCISE 4C

AU 1 Jasmine did a survey of how many of her class had a school lunch one day.

She drew this pie chart.

a Jasmine said that $\frac{1}{3}$ of the students did not have a school lunch.

How does the pie chart show this?

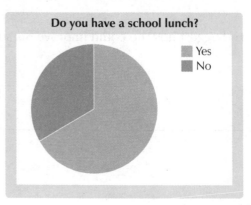

Do you have a school lunch?

Yes
No

_____

_____

b Does the pie chart show how many students were in the survey? _____

c Jasmine said that 18 students had school lunch. How many did not have school lunch?

_____

d Do you think that a pie chart for your class will look similar or different?

Give a reason for your answer.

_____

e Why is a pie chart a good way to compare your class with Jasmine's?

_____

2 Maxwell has been asked to do a survey of what things teenagers in his school are doing to recycle waste.

He has decided to ask this question:

How frequently do you recycle empty drink cans? Tick one box.

Always ☐   Never ☐

a What is wrong with the response boxes for this question?

_____

b Suggest some other boxes that people could fill in.

_____

c Compare your answer to the person next to you. Improve your answer if you can.

3 Surveys often ask people to circle a number when they answer a question.

Here is an example:

How satisfied were you with the service you received from the sales assistant today?

Not satisfied at all   1   2   3   4   5   Very satisfied

a What are some advantages of this system?

_____

_____

b How could you use this method for the survey question in question 2?

_____

_____

Extension

Work with a partner on these questions.

FM 1 The local council wants to compare the number of people in different age groups using a leisure centre.

They have asked for your help.

Hint: do not have too many. Make sure you cover all possibilities.

a What age groups would you suggest for a survey?

_____

_____

b On a separate piece of paper, design a question and response section about age to include in a questionnaire.

c Why might a pie chart be a good way to show the results?

_____

_____

d The council suggest you do the survey on a Friday morning.

Why might this give biased results?

_____

_____

FM 2 This pie chart shows the estimated proportion of people employed in different industries in the UK in 2006.

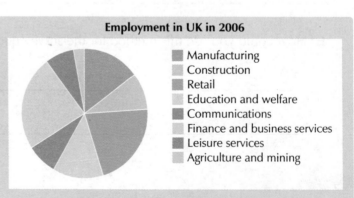

Employment in UK in 2006

Manufacturing
Construction
Retail
Education and welfare
Communications
Finance and business services
Leisure services
Agriculture and mining

Suppose that you have been asked to contribute to a discussion on employment opportunities for young people.

What points could you make based on this pie chart?

Suggest four or five statements you could make.

_____

_____

_____

_____

_____

When you have finished, compare your findings with other students.

Hint: what industries have the largest and smallest numbers of jobs?

Hint: can you give approximate fractions or percentages for the number of jobs in different industries?

checklist

☐ I can interpret and draw pie charts.

☐ I can criticise questionnaires.

☐ I can interpret pie charts and questionnaires in real situations.

Every 10 years there is a census in Great Britain. Information is collected about every person in the country to obtain accurate population estimates.

These can be used for future planning of housing, health care, education and social services. It will help the government decide where to spend money.

1 North East of England

The pie chart for the North East shows the population distribution.

There are four age groups.

a Which age group would you be in?

b Which age group has the largest number of people?

c Which age group has the smallest number of people?

d Can you say how many people are in each age group?

2 London

The pie chart for London shows the same age groups.

a Which age group in London has the largest number of people?

b Roughly what percentage of people in London are under 20?

c Roughly what percentage of people in London are 60 or over?

3 Compare the North East and London

a Which of the two regions has a larger proportion of over 60s?

b Which of the two regions has a larger proportion of people in the age group 20–39?

c We can assume that most working people are in the age range 20–59. Which region has a larger proportion of people in this age range?

4 Birmingham and Torbay

There are two more population pie charts, one is for Birmingham, the other is for Torbay, a region on the south coast of Devon.

Imagine that you are working for the government and you are looking at spending needs in these two areas.

You have been asked to describe the differences between them.

a Which region will need to spend a greater proportion of its income on education and children's services? Explain your answer.

b Which region will need to spend a greater proportion of its income on care for the elderly, such as residential homes and hospitals? Explain your answer.

c Are there any other differences between the pie charts?

d What do you think are the reasons why the pie charts for these areas look different?

Age groups

■	0–19
□	20–39
□	40–59
■	60 and over

The North East

22%   25%
26%   27%

Birmingham

19%   29%
22%   30%

London

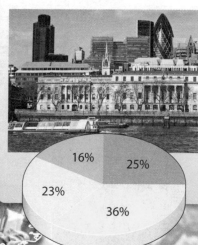

16%   25%
23%   36%

Torbay

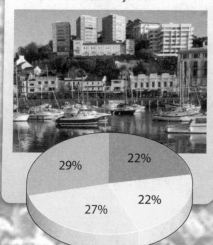

29%   22%
27%   22%

The first census was in 1801

It was undertaken because of fears that there would not be enough food for a growing population. It asked five questions and counted about 2 million people.

The 2001 census asked 40 questions and counted almost 60 million people.

All the figures in this section are from the 2001 Census.

Source: *The Office of National Statistics*

Number: Percentages

5.1 **Fractions, percentages and decimals**

In this section you will learn how to:
- identify the equivalence between fractions, decimals and percentages.

Key words
decimal
fraction
percentage

WORKED EXAMPLE

Put these numbers in order, starting with the smallest.

$$\frac{5}{8}, \quad 65\%, \quad \frac{3}{5}, \quad 0.7, \quad 0.61$$

Solution

The easiest way is to change all the numbers to percentages.

$\frac{5}{8} \times 100 = 62.5\%$ ————————→ Multiply the fraction by 100 on your calculator or work out $5 \div 8 \times 100$.

$\frac{3}{5} \times 100 = 60\%$

$0.7 \times 100 = 70\%$ ————————→ Multiply the decimal by 100.

$0.61 \times 100 = 61\%$

The percentages in order are 60%, 61%, 62.5%, 65% and 70%.

So the numbers are $\frac{3}{5}$, 0.61, $\frac{5}{8}$, 65% and 0.7.

Hint: if you need to find $\frac{3}{5}$ of 100 **without** a calculator, you can do $100 \div 5 = 20$ and then $20 \times 3 = 60$.

EXERCISE 5A

1 70% of this pie chart is red. What percentage is purple?

_____

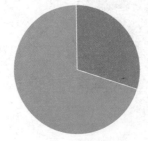

2 37% of the top bar is purple.
10% of the bottom bar is purple.

What percentages are blue?

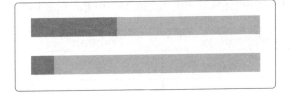

_____

3 **a** What **fractions** does this pie chart show? _____ and _____

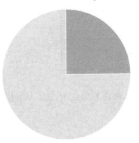

b What **percentages** does the pie chart show? _____ and _____

4 Fill in the gaps in this table.

Decimal	Percentage
0.5	50%
0.3	
0.7	
0.75	
0.15	
	45%

5 This pie chart shows three percentages. What **fractions** does it show?

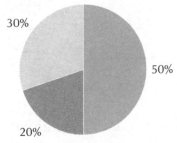

30%

50%

20%

Hint: 30% = $\frac{30}{100}$ and you can simplify this fraction.

Write them as simply as possible.

_____

6 Fill in the gaps in this table. Write the fractions as simply as possible.

Percentage	Fraction
50%	$\frac{1}{2}$
25%	
75%	
20%	
10%	
90%	

Hint: change the fractions to percentages.

AU 7 Which is largest: $\frac{7}{8}$, $\frac{4}{5}$ or 85%? Give a reason for your answer.

_____

8 Sally saves 65% of her pocket money each week. What percentage does she spend?

9 Put the following numbers in order of size starting with the smallest.

8% $\frac{3}{10}$ 0.63 $\frac{4}{5}$ 0.35   70%   _____

Hint: change the decimals and fractions to percentages, then compare them.

Extension

1 What percentage of the following shapes are **unshaded**?

a   b   c   d

_____   _____   _____   _____

2

Cat facts
- 40% of people named cats as their favourite pet.
- 98% of women said they would rather go out with someone who liked cats.
- About $7\frac{1}{2}$ million families have a cat.
- $\frac{1}{4}$ of cat owners keep a cat because cats are easy to look after.

   a Write 40% as a fraction. Give your fraction in its simplest form. _____

   b Write 98% as a decimal. _____

   c Write 7½ million in figures. _____

   d Write $\frac{1}{4}$ as a percentage. _____

   e What percentage of people did not name cats their favourite pet? _____

(Total 5 marks)

Edexcel, June 2005, Paper 1 Foundation, Question 7

5.2 Calculation of percentages

In this section you will learn how to:
● calculate a percentage of a given quantity.

Key words
decrease
increase
percentage

WORKED EXAMPLE

In a sale, the price of a TV is reduced by 15%. Originally it was £390.

What is the sale price?

Solution

First find the reduction.

15% of £390 = 0.15 × £390 = £58.50 ⟶ Change the percentage to a decimal and multiply.

The sale price is £390 − £58.50 = £331.50. ⟶ Check with a calculator. The calculator will not show the final digit but you must write it in.

If you have a percentage button on your calculator, experiment to see if you can use that to find 15% of £390 correctly.

EXERCISE 5B

In this exercise you may use a calculator unless you are asked not to.

1 You should recognise some simple percentages and fractions.

Draw lines to match these percentages and fractions

$\frac{1}{2}$ 10%

$\frac{1}{4}$ 25%

$\frac{3}{4}$ 50%

$\frac{1}{10}$ 75%

2 Calculate these percentages. The first one has been done for you.

a 65% of £120 = 0.65 × 120 = £78   **b** 45% of £80 = _____

c 12% of £500 = _____   **d** 95% of £80 = _____

e 9% of £72 = _____   **f** 3% of £245 = _____

3 Complete this percentages table without using a calculator.

Hint: remember 5% + 10% = 15%.

	5%	10%	15%
£180		£18	
£320	£16		
£600			

4 Find these percentages without using a calculator.

Hint: use the fractions in question 3 to help you.

a 50% of 26 kg = _____

b 25% of 80 m = _____

c 75% of 48 cars = _____

d 50% of 900 drivers = _____

5 Find these percentages. Use a calculator if you need to.

   a 30% of 2000 vehicles = _____

   b 75% of 200 tonnes = _____

   c 14% of £812 = _____

AU 6 | **6% of £420 is £25.20**

   a Can you use this fact to write down 12% of £420? *It should be easy.* _____

   b Can you write down another similar fact?

   _____

7 A school has 850 pupils. 56% are girls.

   a What percentage are boys? _____

   b How many pupils are girls? _____

   c How many pupils are boys? _____

8 There are **3600 spectators** at a football match.

Fill in the missing numbers in this table.

	Percentage	Number
Men	42%	
Women	23%	
Teenagers	19%	
Young children		

9 Carol earns £24 000 a year. She gets a 4% pay rise. How much is that?

_____

Extension

1 A table used to cost £420 but the price has been increased by 8%.

What is the new price? _____

Hint: first find 8% of £420.

2 In a sale, the price of a coat is reduced by 40%.

The original price was £180.

What is the sale price? _____

3 What percentage of £600 is £300? _____

Hint: first think what **fraction** it is.

4 Andrew got 42 out of 50 marks in a history test.

He got 48 out of 60 marks in a geography test.

The marks for each test were changed to a percentage.

In which test did Andrew get the higher mark?

You must show your calculations.

_____

(Total 4 marks)

Edexcel, June 2008, Paper 13 Foundation, Question 12

5.3 Using percentages

In this section you will learn how to:
● understand the use of percentages in everyday situations.

Key words
decrease
increase
percentage

WORKED EXAMPLE

Frank is counting the cars that are speeding outside his block of flats.
On Monday, 65 out of 89 were speeding.
On Tuesday, 91 out of 163 were speeding.
Which day was worse?

Solution

First write the numbers as **fractions**.

Monday was $\frac{65}{89}$.　　Tuesday was $\frac{91}{163}$.

Now change them to **percentages**.

Monday was $\frac{65}{89} \times 100 = 73.0\%$. ⟶ Check this with a calculator

Tuesday was $\frac{91}{163} \times 100 = 55.8\%$.

Monday was worse. ⟶ Percentages make comparison easy

EXERCISE 5C

1 Elle scored 17 out of 20 in a test.

  a Write that as a fraction. _____

  b What percentage is that? _____

FM 2 '9 out of 10 cats prefer Chunkee cat food' says the advert.

  What percentage is that? _____

FM **3** Jen achieved these marks in tests in different subjects.

Subject	Mark	Percentage
Chinese	18 out of 25	
Catering	21 out of 30	
Engineering	40 out of 50	
Environmental Studies	67 out of 100	

a Change the marks to percentages.

b In which subject did she have the best score? _____

FM **4** A cereal box usually holds 300 grams. The box says '25% extra free'.

a What is 25% of 300 grams? _____

b How much is in the box now? _____

FM **5** A shampoo bottle usually holds 240 ml. It says '50% extra free'.

What is the contents, including the extra free amount? _____

6 Biscuits are being sold with 15% extra free. The usual weight was 240 grams.

What is the weight, including the extra biscuits? _____

AU **7** Would you rather be given 20% of £60 or 60% of £20?

_____

8 Claudine thinks it rains on 1 day out of 2. Riley thinks it is 2 out of 5.
Lola says it is 6 out of 10.

Change these numbers to percentages.

a 1 out of 2 = _____   **b** 2 out of 5 = _____

c 6 out of 10 = _____

Extension

FM 1 'Buy 5 tins of cat food for the price of 4' says the supermarket offer.
Carly says that is the same as 25% extra free.

Do you agree? Give a reason for your answer. _____

_____

FM 2 These pie charts show
the population of the UK and
of London in the 2001
census.

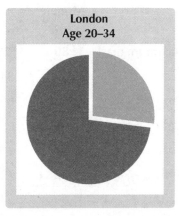

UK
Age 20–34

London
Age 20–34

a Approximately what
proportion of the
population of the UK is
between 20 and 34 years
old? Circle the correct
answer.

10%   20%   30%   40%

b Approximately what proportion of the population of the London is between
20 and 34 years old? Circle the correct answer.

16%   26%   40%   50%

c Jonah says, "The charts show that there are more people aged between 20 and 34
in London than there are in the rest of the UK." Explain why this is incorrect.

_____

_____

d Complete this sentence:

The proportion of people aged 20–34 is _____ in London than it is in
the UK as a whole.

e Why do you think this is the case? _____

_____

checklist

☐ I can identify the equivalence between fractions, decimals and percentages.

☐ I can calculate a percentage of a given quantity.

☐ I can understand the use of percentages in everyday situations.

A group of college students are taking a course which has three modules.

Here are their marks.

	Module 1	Module 2	Module 3
Maximum mark	80	120	150
Aziz	66	84	102
Barry	56	66	111
Claire	60	99	120
Donna	54	66	96
Emily	72	72	80
Franz	56	54	87

Task A

The students want to compare their marks for each module.

They can do this by changing them to percentages.

Example:

For module 1 Aziz scored:
$$\frac{66}{80} = 0.825 = 82.5\%$$
For module 2 Aziz scored:
$$\frac{84}{120} = 0.7 = 70\%$$

	Module 1	Module 2	Module 3
Aziz	82.5%	70%	
Barry			
Claire			
Donna			
Emily			
Franz			

1 Fill in the percentages in this table.

Each module has a pass mark of 50%.

2 Who has **not** passed all three modules?

Task B

This graph shows the percentages.

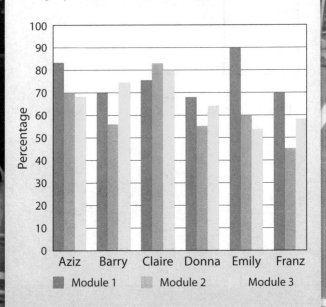

Use the graph to answer these questions. Discuss your answers with a partner.

1   Which module do you think was the easiest of the three? Give a reason for your answer

2   Who had the most **consistent** set of results?
    This means similar results for all three modules.
    Give a reason for your answer.

Task C

The five who have passed all the modules need to know their overall percentages.

Barry worked out his like this.

   Total = 56 + 66 + 111 = 233

   Maximum possible = 80 + 120 + 150 = 350

   Overall percentage = 233 ÷ 350 = 0.6657…
   = 66.6% rounded to 1 decimal place

1   Find the other percentages and put them in this table.

	Total mark out of 350	Overall percentage
Aziz		
Barry	233	66.6%
Claire		
Donna		
Emily		
Franz		

Anyone with an overall 75% or more is awarded a Distinction.

2   Who will be awarded a Distinction?

6 Algebra: Using algebra

Writing expressions

In this section you will learn how to:	Key word
• form algebraic expressions.	expression

WORKED EXAMPLE

This is a square. Each side is A cm long.

Here are two squares the same size put together.

Write expressions for the areas in cm² of the square and the rectangle.

Solution

The area of the square $= \text{length} \times \text{width}$
$= A \times A = A^2$

The rectangle is two squares, so it is double the area of one square.

Area of rectangle $= 2A^2$.  This is a short way to write $2 \times A^2$.

EXERCISE 6A

1 Simone is 16 years old.

What are the ages of these people?

a Ahmed, who is three years older than Simone. _____

b George, who is half Simone's age. _____

c Cyril, who is twice Simone's age. _____

FM Functional Maths **AU** (AO2) Assessing Understanding **PS** (AO3) Problem Solving

2 Rex is R years old.

Write an expression using R to write these ages. The first one is done for you.

a Keri is 5 years younger than Rex. $R - 5$

b Lucy is 4 years older than Rex.   _____

c Rich is twice Rex's age.   _____

d Jose is half Rex's age.   _____

3 Jack is K years old.

Write these expressions in words.

a Fatima is $K + 7$ _____

b Will is $K - 2$ _____

c Aya is $3K$ _____

d Lachan is $K \div 2$ _____

4 James packs books into boxes.

He packs 20 books into each box.

James packs x boxes of books.

Write an expression, in terms of x, for the number of books he packs.

_____   (1)

(Total 1 marks)

Edexcel, November 2007, Paper 10 Foundation, Question 7

5 If $w = 6$, what is the value of these expressions?

a $w + 9 =$ _____   **b** $w - 5 =$ _____   **c** $w \div 2 =$ _____

d $w - 8 =$ _____   **e** $2w =$ _____   **f** $5w =$ _____

6 $p = 4$ and $q = 6$. Find the values of these. The first one is done for you.

a $5p + 2q =$ ___20 + 12 = 32___

b $5p - 2q =$ _____

c $10p + 3q =$ _____

d $\frac{1}{2}p + \frac{1}{2}q =$ _____

e $2q - p =$ _____

f $5q + p + 7 =$ _____

Extension

PS **1** This is a square. Each side is L cm long.

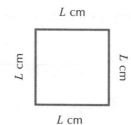

L cm

L cm

L cm

L cm

a Explain why the perimeter in cm is $4L$.

_____

Here are two of the squares put together.

b Write an expression for the perimeter in cm. _____

2 If $F = 4$ and $G = 6$, find these expressions.

a $3F + 3G =$ _____

b $3(F + G) =$ _____

c Explain why they are the same.

_____

3 The sides of the green rectangle are
a and *b*.

The perimeter of the green shape is
$b + a + b + a$
$= 2b + 2a$.

> **Note:** starting at the top
> and going clockwise.

The perimeter of the orange shape is
$4b + a + 2b + 2a + 2b + 3a$

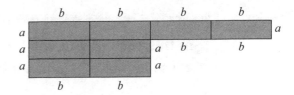

This can be simplified to $8b + 6a$
(or you can write $6a + 8b$).

a Write an expression for the perimeter of each of these shapes as simply as possible.

Perimeter of A = _____   Perimeter of B = _____

b Draw your own shape with a perimeter of $6a + 8b$ on this grid.

c Compare your drawing with your neighbour's.
Are they the same or different?   _____

6.2 Formulas

In this section you will learn how to:
● use formulas in different situations.

Key word
formula

WORKED EXAMPLE

A mobile phone contract costs £10.50 a month and then there is a charge of 4 pence for every text.
Find a formula to work out the cost of a number of texts.
Use it to find the cost of 247 texts in a month.

Solution

The formula is: cost = number of texts × the charge per text + monthly fee
We need to be careful not to mix pence and pounds.

Let's use pounds.

Cost in pounds = number of texts × 0.04 + 10.50 ⟶ 4p is £0.04

Now for 247 texts, cost in pounds = 247 × 0.04 + 10.50 ⟶ Use a calculator.

= £20.38

EXERCISE 6B

1 A formula for estimating the perimeter of a circular pond is:

Perimeter = 3 × diameter

a What is the perimeter of a pond with diameter of 4 m? _____

b What is the perimeter of a pond with diameter of 6 m? _____

2 The formula for finding the total cost in pounds of entry to a zoo for adults and children is:

T = 20 × number of adults + 15 × number of children

a What is the total cost for a family of 1 adult and 2 children? _____

b What is the total cost for a family of 2 adults and 3 children? _____

3 The formula for finding the perimeter of a triangle with sides of length a, b, and c is:

$$P = a + b + c$$

a What is the perimeter of a triangle when $a = 3$ cm, $b = 4$ cm, and $c = 5$ cm?

_____

b What is the perimeter of a triangle when $a = 12$ m, $b = 6$ m, and $c = 9$ m?

_____

4 A phone contract gives 100 free texts a week and then charges 5 pence per text.

What will be the cost of the following? **Hint:** work out how many texts over 100 were sent.

a 90 texts _____

b 120 texts _____

c 200 texts _____

5 The cost in pounds of hiring a car is given by the formula:

Cost = 20 × Number of days + 10

What will it cost for the following?

a 2 days _____

b 4 days _____

6 The cooking time in minutes to roast a chicken is:

40 × weight in kg + 20

How long should you cook a chicken of these weights?

a 2 kg _____

b 1.5 kg _____

c 1.8 kg _____

Extension

PS **1** The cost in pounds of hiring a boat for a party is:

number of people × 6 + 125

Hoda hired the boat for her 18th birthday party. It cost her £365. How many people were at the party?

Hint: you could start with a guess and then see if you can improve it.

_____

2 A can of cola costs *x* pence.

An ice cream costs *y* pence.

Atif buys 3 cans of cola and 2 ice creams.

Write down an expression in terms of *x* and *y*, for the total cost, in pence.

_____ (2)

(Total 2 marks)

Edexcel, March 2008, Paper 9 Foundation, Question 9

6.3 Using formulas

In this section you will learn how to:
● use formulas in a real-life situation.

Key words
expression
formula

EXERCISE 6C

FM 1 A cookery book gives these recommendations for roasting beef. Use this information in questions a to c.

> Cook it for 40 minutes per kilogram.
>
> Then add this extra time, depending on how well cooked you want it:
>
> Rare: add 15 minutes
>
> Medium rare: add 30 minutes
>
> Well done: add 45 minutes

a Josh wants to cook a 1.5 kg joint well done. What is the cooking time?

_____

b Complete this table to show cooking times in minutes.

	1 kg	1.5 kg	2 kg	2.5 kg
Rare				
Medium rare				
Well done				

c Here is a formula for cooking a rare joint of beef:

Cooking time in minutes = weight in kilograms × 40 + 15

Write a formula for cooking it well done.

_____

FM 2 Rania is a computer expert who will visit your home to repair your computer. She will charge £30 to visit plus £24 for every hour she is at your house. Use this information in questions a to d.

a Complete this formula for Rania's charges:

Cost in pounds = length of visit in hours × _____ **+** _____

b What would Rania charge for a visit lasting $1\frac{1}{2}$ hours?

_____

c When Rania fixed Riley's computer, she charged him £102. How long did it take her?

_____

d Put some numbers in this table to show much Rania will charge for different visits.

Length of visit in hours	1 hour			
Cost in £				

Extension

FM 1 A music festival organiser is hiring a set of laser lights. Here is a table of costs.

Number of days	1	2	3	4
Cost in pounds	£90	£100	£110	£120

a What do you think the cost would be for 5 days? _____

b Find a formula to work out the cost in pounds for any number of days.

Hint: you need to multiply by one number and add another one.

_____

checklist

☐ I can form algebraic expressions.

☐ I can use formulas in different situations.

☐ I can use formulas in a real-life situation.

Functional Maths
Mobile phone deals

Here are three mobile phone deals available on a particular model. They are all on the basis of a 12-month contract.

In each deal, every month you pay:

- a monthly rental charge
- the cost of the minutes of calls over a certain number
- the cost of the number of texts over a certain number.

SuperDeal A

Monthly rental	Free minutes per month	Free texts per month	Cost of calls per minute	Cost of texts
£24.47	150	150	30p	12p

SuperDeal B

Monthly rental	Free minutes per month	Free texts per month	Cost of calls per minute	Cost of texts
£29.36	300	200	30p	12p

SuperDeal C

Monthly rental	Free minutes per month	Free texts per month	Cost of calls per minute	Cost of texts
£34.25	500	375	30p	12p

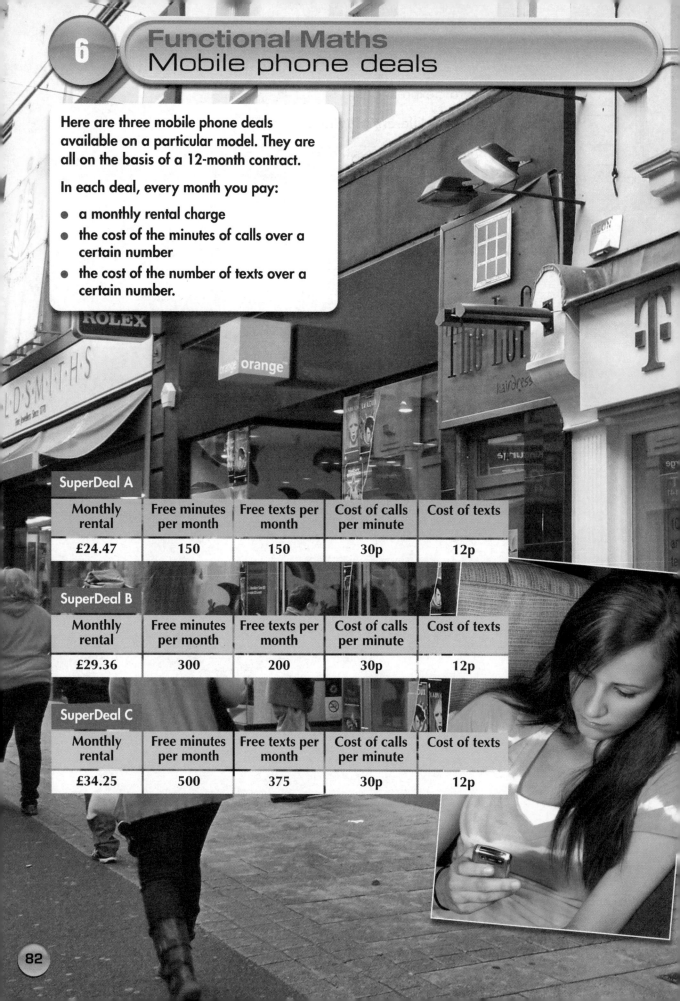

Task

1 Complete the table showing the monthly cost for texts only.

SuperDeal A

Texts in a month	0	50	100	150	200	250	300	350	400
Cost in pounds	24.47	24.47			30.47				

Hint: remember you only pay for the number of texts over 150.

SuperDeal B

Texts in a month	0	50	100	150	200	250	300	350	400
Cost in pounds	29.36								

Hint: when do you start paying extra on this deal?

SuperDeal C

Texts in a month	0	50	100	150	200	250	300	350	400
Cost in pounds									

2 Katie does not make many calls but she sends a lot of texts. The calls she makes will be free. She wants to compare the 3 deals for texts only.

The best deal depends on how many texts Katie sends in a month.

What advice would you give her about the best deal for her?

3 Mr Jackson wants to use his phone to make calls only.

He will not send many texts so they will be free.

The chart below shows the cost of each deal if you only use the phone for calls.

Use the chart to decide on the best deal for Mr Jackson.

Hint: it will depend on how many minutes of calls he makes each month.

4 Imagine you are getting a new mobile phone contract.

Decide which would be the best deal for you – A, B or C.

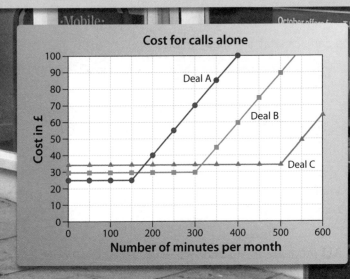

Cost for calls alone

7 Statistics: Averages

Averages and spread

In this section you will learn how to:
- find the mode, median and range of a distribution and understand what they show.

Key words
average
frequency
median
mode
range

WORKED EXAMPLE

Here are the scores out of 10 for a group of gymnasts doing an exercise.

8	7	4	9	7	6	9	10	3	8
9	9	10	4	10	9	9	9	7	7

What are the median, the mode and the range?

Solution

To find the median, you must put the numbers in order:

3 4 4 6 7 7 7 7 8 8 9 9 9 9 9 9 9 10 10 10

The **median** is the middle score. Because there are 20 numbers there, is not a middle one. The median is therefore halfway between the 10th and the 11th score.

10th score = 8 and 11th score = 9 so the **median is 8.5**.

The **mode** is the most common score. You can see that the **mode is 9**.

The **range** is the spread of the scores. It is the largest minus the smallest, which is 10 − 3, so the **range is 7**.

FM Functional Maths **AU** (AO2) Assessing Understanding **PS** (AO3) Problem Solving

EXERCISE 7A

1 Some people were asked which colour of the rainbow they liked best.

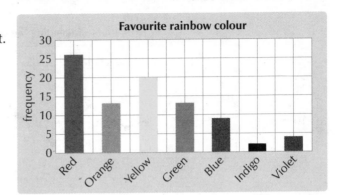

Favourite rainbow colour

a How many chose yellow?

_____

b Which was the least popular colour?

_____

c What colour was the mode? _____

2 Some young people were asked which sport they enjoyed playing most.

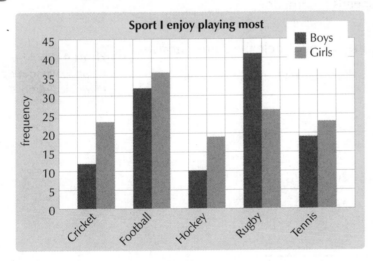

Sport I enjoy playing most

a List the sports in order of popularity for girls.

_____

b What was the mode for girls? _____

c What was the mode for boys? _____

3 A survey was carried out of speeds of drivers exceeding the speed limit outside a school. Here are the results.

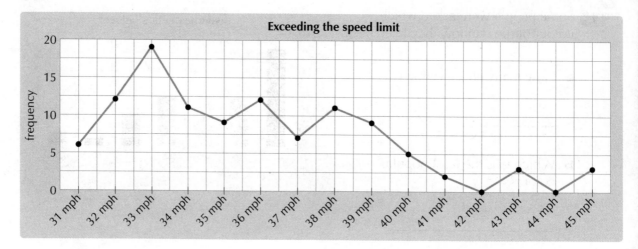

a What speed was the mode? _____

b What was the range of speeds recorded? _____

c How many cars were in the survey? Circle the correct answer.

14   15   19   20   109

Hint: it should be obvious without doing any calculations!

4 Here are fifteen numbers.

10	12	13	15	15
17	19	20	20	20
21	25	25	25	25

a Find the mode.   _____   (1)

b Find the median.   _____   (1)

c Work out the range. _____   (2)

(Total 4 marks)

Edexcel, November 2008, Paper 5/8 Foundation, Question 1

5 These are the hourly rates of pay for seven people.

£6.50   £6.74   £7.52   £8.72   £9.13   £9.48   £10.21

a What is the median? _____   **b** What is the range? _____

Two more people add their rates of pay to the list. They are £9.72 and £10.03.

c What is the median now? _____   **d** What is the range now? _____

Extension

1 Here are the ages of 25 young people in a frequency table.

Age	Frequency
15 years	6
16 years	4
17 years	5
18 years	10

a What age is the mode? _____

b What is the range of the ages?

_____

c What is the median age? _____

Hint: you must find the middle number out of 25 ages.

2 Here is a stem-and-leaf diagram for a set of 17 test marks.

```
1 | 7   8
2 | 0   0   4   6   7   9
3 | 0   3   5   5   8
4 | 1   1   2   2
```

Key: 3 | 0 stands for 30

a The lowest mark is 17. What is the highest mark? _____

b What is the range of the marks? _____   **c** What is the median mark? _____

3 Here are Indira's waiting times for the bus on 10 days.

3 minutes	4 minutes	4 minutes	4 minutes	6 minutes
8 minutes	8 minutes	9 minutes	9 minutes	9 minutes

What is the median time? _____

Hint: what do you do if there is no middle number?

7.2 The mean

In this section you will learn how to:
- calculate the mean
- recognise that an average can be a mode, a median or a mean.

Key words
average
mean
median
mode

WORKED EXAMPLE

Here are the salaries of 7 employees in a small firm.

£15 000   £17 400   £17 800   £21 200   £23 500   £29 200   £49 300

What are the mean and the median?

What is the better average to use?

Solution

To find the mean add up the 7 salaries and divide by 7. ⟶ Use a calculator

That is 173 400 ÷ 7 = £24 771. ⟶ To the nearest pound

The median is the middle one = £21 200.

Both the mean and the median are averages. It might be better to use the median in this case. Three people earn more than the median and three people earn less.

The mean is distorted by one salary which is much larger than all the rest.

EXERCISE 7B

Use a calculator for these questions.

1 Here are Indira's waiting times for the bus on 10 days.

3 minutes	4 minutes	4 minutes	4 minutes	6 minutes
8 minutes	8 minutes	9 minutes	9 minutes	9 minutes

What is the mean waiting time? _____

2 Find the mean of these five cricket scores.

13   21   0   8   11   _____

3 Here are the weights of five suitcases.

19 kg   16 kg   21 kg   17 kg   22 kg

a Find the mean weight. _____ kg   b What is the range? _____ kg

AU 4 Here are numbers of children in some families.

1	3	3	4	2	5	6	3	2	3
3	2	4	3	3	5	1	2	3	3

a How many families are there? _____   b What is the mean number of children? _____

c What is the mode? _____   d What is the median family size? _____

e What is the average family size? _____

AU 5 Here are the heights of some young children in centimetres.

Girls 85   73   66   80   82   77   65   72

Boys 71   83   92   78   85

a What is the mean height and the median height of the girls? _____

b What is the mean height and the median height of the boys? _____

c On average who are taller, the girls or the boys? Give a reason for your answer.

_____

d What is the range of the girls' heights? _____

e What is the range of the boys' heights? _____

6 The table shows some information about five children.

Name	Gender	Age	Hair colour
Aaron	Male	6	Black
Becky	Female	10	Brown
Kim	Female	6	Brown
Darren	Male	9	Blonde
Emily	Female	4	Red

a Write down the colour of Darren's hair.   _____   (1)

b Write down the name of the oldest child.   _____   (1)

c Work out the mean of the ages of the children.   _____   (2)

(Total 4 marks)

Edexcel, June 2008, Paper 5/8 Foundation, Question 1

Extension

AU 1 The mean weight of 50 boys is 45 kilograms.

Just one of these statements must be true. Which one? Give a reason for your answer.

A   Half the boys weigh more than 45 kilograms.

B   The total weight of the boys is 2250 kilograms.

C   The boys are overweight.

Answer: _____

2 Here are the times, in minutes, that Myra waited for a train on 9 occasions:

2   3   4   6   7   9   12   13   52

a What was the mean waiting time? _____

b On one occasion she missed the train and had to
wait for the next one. Which number do you think that was? _____

c Ignore the 52 and find the mean of the 8 remaining numbers. _____

d How much has the mean changed? _____

e Find the median of the 9 waiting times. _____

f Ignore the 52 and find the median of the 8 remaining numbers. _____

g How much has the median changed? _____

7.3 Using statistics

In this section you will learn how to:
● use the mode, median, mean or range in realistic situations.

Key words
mean
median
mode
range

EXERCISE 7C

1 Here are the goals scored by Norwich and Yeovil football clubs in the first nine matches of a season.

Norwich	1	4	1	1	5	1	2	0	1
Yeovil	2	0	1	1	3	1	1	0	2

a What is the mean for each club? Norwich _____ Yeovil _____

b What is the median for each club? Norwich _____ Yeovil _____

Hint: remember to put the numbers in order first.

c Write a sentence comparing the mean and the median for each club.

_____

2 Here are the journey times in minutes for Jowar's journeys to work in April.

32	33	33	35	38	38	38	38	39	42
42	43	45	48	48	49	50	51	51	66

a What is the mean time? _____ minutes

b What is the median time? _____ minutes

c What time is the mode? _____ minutes

d Jowar said that his average time was 42 minutes. Was he correct?
Give a reason for your answer.

_____

e What was the range of times? _____ minutes

f In May, the median time was 49 minutes and the range was
21 minutes. Compare the journey times for April and May.

Hint: compare the two medians and the two ranges.

_____

_____

PS 3 Three runners regularly run half marathons together. They want to compare their times.
They each find their median and their range. Here are the results.

	Median	Range
Petra	1 hour 48 minutes	52 minutes
Louise	2 hours 12 minutes	23 minutes
Klara	1 hour 39 minutes	31 minutes

a Who is the fastest runner? Give a reason for your answer.

_____

b Who is the most consistent runner? Give a reason for your answer.

_____

4 Here are the median salaries for six different jobs in the UK. 'Average salary' for a job usually means the median.

a Which job in the table has the lowest average salary?

_____

Job	Median salary
Office Administrator	£15 370
Office Manager	£20 649
Retail Store Manager	£21 319
IT Project Manager	£39 695
Software Engineer	£27 519

b Which job in the table has the highest average salary?

_____

c Complete this sentence:
Half the Retail Store Managers in the UK earn _____.

Hint: use the median salary to help you.

5 Here are the average monthly temperatures in Miami, Florida.
The temperatures are in degrees F, not degrees C, because they use that system in the USA.

Jan	Feb	Mar	Apr	May	Jun	Jul	Aug	Sep	Oct	Nov	Dec
67	68	72	75	79	81	83	83	82	77	73	69

a What is the range? _____

b What is the mean? _____

c What is the median? _____

d If you were asked for the average temperature in Florida, what would you say?
Give a reason for your answer.

_____

Extension

1 You saw this stem-and-leaf diagram for a set of 17 test marks in the Extension exercise in section 11.1.

1	7	8				
2	0	0	4	6	7	9
3	0	3	5	5	8	
4	1	1	2	2		

Key: 3 | 0 stands for 30

Use it to find the mean test mark.

Hint: first add up 17 + 18 + 20 + 20 + ...

_____

FM 2 Here are the statistics about some of children's weights.

	Boys	Girls
Number of children	278	345
Median weight	42 kg	47 kg
Mean weight	40.825 kg	47.139 kg
Mode weight	39 kg	50 kg
Range	8 kg	21 kg

Use the information in the table to describe the differences between the boys and the girls in this survey.

_____

_____

_____

checklist

☐ I can find the mode, median and range of a distribution and understand what they show.

☐ I can calculate the mean.

☐ I can recognise that an average can be a mode, a median or a mean.

☐ I can use the mode, median, mean or range in realistic situations.

Problem Solving
Goal!

These tables show the football results for one weekend in 2009.

Premier League			Total
Birmingham	0-1	Aston Villa	1
Blackburn	3-1	Wolves	4
Fulham	2-1	Everton	3
Liverpool	4-2	Burnley	6
Man City	4-2	Arsenal	6
Portsmouth	2-3	Bolton	5
Stoke	1-2	Chelsea	3
Sunderland	4-1	Hull	5
Tottenham	1-3	Man United	4
Wigan	1-0	West Ham	1
		Goals	38

League 1			Total
Bristol R	1-0	Oldham	
Carlisle	0-2	Brighton	
Charlton	1-2	Southampton	
Gillingham	2-0	Millwall	
Hartlepool	1-1	Wycombe	
Huddersfield	0-0	Brentford	
Leyton O	1-1	Exeter	
MK Dons	2-1	Norwich	
Southend	0-0	Leeds	
Swindon	1-1	Colchester	
Tranmere	2-3	Walsall	
Yeovil	2-2	Stockport	
		Goals	

Interesting fact

Mean goals per match
= 38 ÷ 10 = 3.8

Championship			Total
Cardiff	0-1	Newcastle	
Coventry	1-1	Bristol City	
Crystal Palace	1-4	Scunthorpe	
Derby	0-1	Sheffield U	
Leicester	2-1	Blackpool	
Middlesbrough	3-1	Ipswich	
Preston	2-0	Swansea	
QPR	1-1	Peterborough	
Reading	0-0	Doncaster R	
Sheffield Wed	1-1	Nottingham F	
Watford	1-0	Barnsley	
WBA	3-1	Plymouth	
		Goals	

League 2			Total
Accrington	2-1	Darlington	
Aldershot	1-1	Port Vale	
Bournemouth	3-1	Lincoln	
Bradford	1-1	Burton	
Bury	0-1	Cheltenham	
Dag & Red	2-1	Chesterfield	
Grimsby	1-0	Hereford	
Macclesfield	1-1	Barnet	
Notts County	5-2	Northampton	
Rochdale	2-1	Torquay	
Rotherham	0-0	Morecambe	
Shrewsbury	2-0	Crewe	
		Goals	

Task A

Does the total number of goals scored in a match vary between different leagues?

Here are some suggestions of things to do to help you answer this question.

1 Find the total goals for each match.
   The Premier League has been done for you.

2 Calculate the mean for each league.
   The Premier League has been done for you.

3 Compare the means for each league.
   Are they similar or different?

Hint: be careful to divide by the correct number of matches. It is not always 10.

Task B

Is the mode of total goals per match for each league the same or different?

Task C

Look up some recent results and compare them with the results given here. Do you come to the same conclusions?

8 Geometry: Area and perimeter

8.1 Perimeter

In this section you will learn how to:
- find and use the perimeter of a shape.

Key words
perimeter
rectangle
square

WORKED EXAMPLE

Here is a sketch of a field.

The perimeter of the field is 205 metres.
The longest side is 75 metres. The opposite side is 40 metres.
The other two sides are the same length.

How long are the other two sides?

Solution

40 + 75 + third + fourth = 205   → The perimeter is the distance all around the field.

115 + third + fourth = 205   → 40 + 75 = 115

Third + fourth = 205 − 115 = 90

The other two sides are both 45 metres.   → Half of 90 is 45

EXERCISE 8A

1 Work out the perimeters of the following shapes.

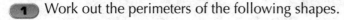

a 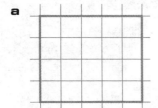   **b**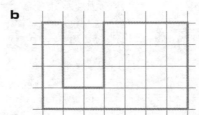

Each square on the grid is 1 cm². Count the squares to find the area.

a Perimeter = _____ cm   **b** Perimeter = _____ cm

2 Find the perimeters of these fields.

a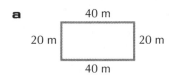

b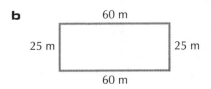

Perimeter = _____ m

Perimeter = _____ m

c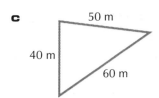

Perimeter = _____ m

AU 3 The perimeter of this triangle is 24 cm.

How long is the third side?

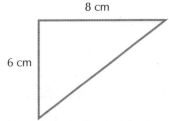

_____ cm

AU 4 A four-sided shape has a perimeter of 20 cm.

Give possible lengths of the four sides. _____

5 Calculate the perimeters of these rectangles.

Hint: write in the two missing lengths.

a

3 cm

5 cm

a Perimeter = _____

b

4 m

5 m

b Perimeter = _____

c

17 mm

1 mm

c Perimeter = _____

FM 6 Mr Williams wants to put a small fence all the way around his vegetable plot. A diagram of the plot is shown below.

4 m

4 m

2 m

6 m

What is the total length of fence he needs?

_____

Extension

AU 1 An equilateral triangle and a square both have a perimeter of 36 cm.

Sketch each shape and write the lengths on each side.

PS 2 Each small square has a perimeter of 20 cm.

What is the perimeter of the large square?

Hint: find the length of each small square.

_____ cm

8.2 Area

In this section you will learn how to:

● calculate the area of rectangles and more complicated shapes.

Key words

area
rectangle
square

WORKED EXAMPLE

Here is a sketch of a garden lawn.

Find the area of the lawn.

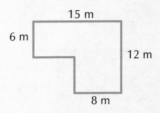

Solution

First divide the shape into rectangles.

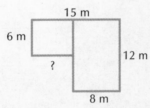

The area of the larger rectangle is $8 \times 12 = 96$ m². ⟶ Don't forget the units.

The length marked with a ? is $15 - 8 = 7$. ⟶ ? + 8 makes 15.

The area of the smaller rectangle is $6 \times 7 = 42$ m².

The total area of the lawn is $96 + 42 = 138$ m². ⟶ **Add** the two areas.

EXERCISE 8B

1 Work out the areas of the following shapes.

a

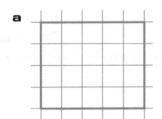

b

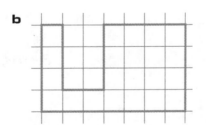

a Area = _____

b Area = _____

2 The map shows a small island.
Each square on the map represents 1 km^2.
Estimate the area of the island.

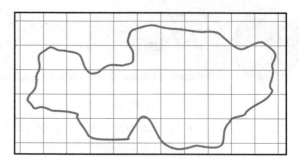

Area = _____

3 A shaded shape is shown on the grid of centimetre squares.

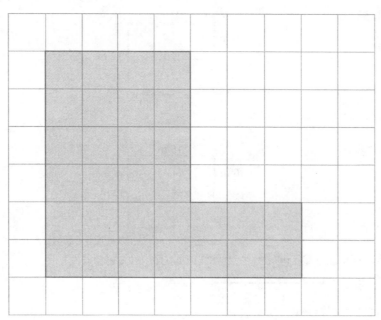

a Find the perimeter of the shaded shape.

_____ cm   (1)

b Find the area of the shaded shape.

_____ cm^2 (1)

(Total 2 marks)

Edexcel, November 2007, Paper 10 Foundation, Question 3

4 Calculate the areas of these rectangles.

Don't forget the units in your answers.

a
3 cm
5 cm

b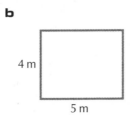
4 m
5 m

c
17 mm
1 mm

a Area = _____

b Area = _____

c Area = _____

5 Here is a rectangle. Diagram not drawn accurately.

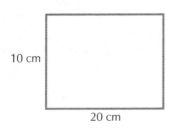
10 cm
20 cm

a Work out the perimeter of the rectangle.

_____ cm   (2)

b Work out the area of the rectangle.

_____ cm^2 (2)

(Total 4 marks)

Edexcel, November 2008, Paper 1 Foundation, Question 12

6 Here is a plan of a vegetable plot.

The plot is divided into two rectangles.

a Find the area of each rectangle.

12 m
6 m
10 m
7 m
4 m
5 m

_____

b Find the area of the vegetable plot.

_____

Extension

FM **1** Jack wants to carpet this floor. He needs to find the area of the floor.
Calculate the area for him.
Show your method.

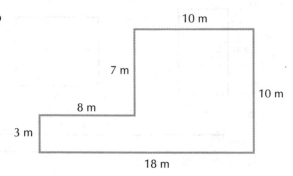

_____

2 **a** Find the area of the rectangle.

_____

b The triangle is half the size of the rectangle.

Find the area of the triangle.

_____

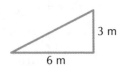

3 Find the areas of these triangles.

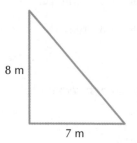

a _____   **b** _____

8.3 Using perimeter and area

In this section you will learn how to:
- calculate perimeter and area in practical situations.

Key words
area
perimeter

WORKED EXAMPLE

Here is a sketch of a garden lawn.

Anish wants to lay new turf and put edging all round the lawn.

Turf costs £3.40 per square metre.

Edging is needed for the border of the lawn. Edging comes in packs of 2 metres. A pack costs £11.

How much will the materials cost?

15 m
6 m
12 m
8 m

Solution

To find the cost of the **turf**, we need to know the **area** of the lawn.

We did that in the example in topic 8.2.

The area is 138 m². ⟶ Look back at the example in 8B to see how to do that.

The turf will cost 138 × £3.40 = £469.20.

To find the cost of the **edging** we need to know the **perimeter** of the lawn.

That is 15 + 12 + 8 + 6 + 7 + 6 = 54 m. ⟶ Can you see where those numbers come from?

The edging is £11 for 2 metres.

54 ÷ 2 = 27 packs needed.

The edging will cost 27 × £11 = £291.

Total cost is £469.20 + £291 = **£760.20.** ⟶ Anish may want to order a little more to allow for wastage. He may also need to pay for delivery.

EXERCISE 8C

You will need a calculator for this exercise.

The dimensions of many games courts and pitches were fixed years ago. They were given as feet or yards. When these are changed into metres, they become awkward decimals.

PS 1 A tennis court is 78 feet long (that is, 23.77 metres).

A singles tennis court is 27 feet wide (that is, 8.23 metres).

a Find the perimeter of a singles tennis court in feet.

_____ feet

b Find the area of a singles tennis court in square feet.

_____ square feet

PS 2 A doubles tennis court is 78 feet long and 36 feet wide.

Find the perimeter and area of a doubles tennis court.

> Remember the units.

a Perimeter = _____

b Area = _____

AU 3 Is a doubles tennis court twice as big as a singles court? Give a reason for your answer.

_____

AU 4 All badminton courts are 44 feet long.

A singles court is 17 feet wide and a doubles court is 20 feet wide.

Find the perimeters and areas of a singles court and a doubles court.

Put units in your answers. **Hint:** the units will be feet or square feet. Draw diagrams to help you.

a Singles court perimeter = _____

Singles court area = _____

b Doubles court perimeter = _____

Doubles court area = _____

FM 5 A hockey pitch is 60 yards (55 metres) long and 100 yards (91.4 metres) wide.

    a The players run around the pitch to warm up. How many yards is that?

                                         Hint: draw a diagram.

    _____

    b The surface of the pitch needs to be replaced. The cost depends on the area. What is the area of a hockey pitch in square yards?

    _____

FM 6 Mike wants a new lawn in his garden.

The dimensions are shown on this diagram.

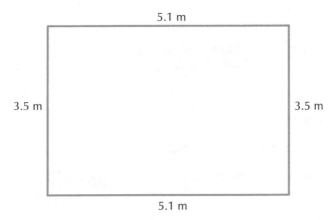

5.1 m

3.5 m   3.5 m

5.1 m

    a Mike wants to grow the lawn from seed.

       To do that, does he need to know the perimeter or the area of the lawn?

    _____

    b Use a calculator to find both the perimeter and the area of Mike's lawn.

       Perimeter = _____

       Area = _____

                                                    Hint: what might you

    c Why might Mike want to know the perimeter of the lawn?   put round a lawn?

    _____

FM 7 This is the floor of a room.

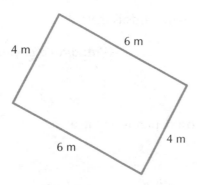

a Jude wants to buy a carpet that costs £8.49 per square metre.

What will the carpet for this room cost? Show your method.

Hint: find the area first.

£_____

b Skirting board goes round the edge of the room.

It costs £20 for a piece of skirting board 2.5 metres long.

How much will it cost to put board around the room?

Show how you got your answer.

Hint: find the perimeter first.

£_____

c You will not need skirting board in front of the door.
Will this make any difference to the cost? Explain.

_____

Extension

FM 1 Mr Waters want to put carpet tiles in his office.

The tiles are 50 cm squares.

They cost £3.49 each.

Here is a plan of his office floor.

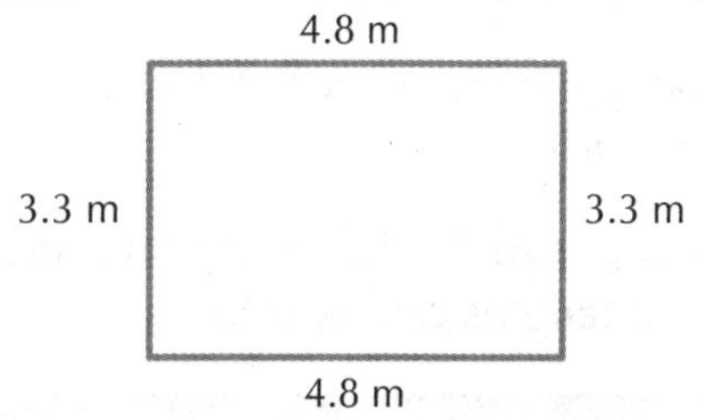

4.8 m

3.3 m   3.3 m

4.8 m

He has asked for your advice about the number of tiles he needs and the cost of buying them.

What can you tell him?

_____

checklist

☐ I can find and use the perimeter of a shape.

☐ I can calculate the area of rectangles and more complicated shapes.

☐ I can calculate perimeter.

You could work with a partner on these tasks.

Surprisingly, there is no fixed size for a football pitch.

The FA suggests the following maximum and minimum lengths and widths.

	Length in metres		Width in metres	
	maximum	minimum	maximum	minimum
Seniors	120	90	90	45.5
Under 16	100.6	82.3	64	45.5
Under 14	91	72.8	56	45.5
Under 12	82	68.25	50.77	42

120 m by 90 m

Task A

1. The table shows that the **maximum** size for a **senior** pitch is 120 metres long and 90 metres wide.

   What are the **maximum** area and perimeter of a senior pitch?

2a. What is the **minimum** size for a **senior** pitch?

 b. What would the area and perimeter of this pitch be?

3. Look at the difference between your answers to questions 1 and 2.

   Would you say there is a **big difference** or a **small difference** between them?

   Discuss your answer with someone else and see if they agree.

Task B

1. Make a **scale drawing** to illustrate the maximum-sized and minimum-sized senior pitches that you looked at in questions 1 and 2 of Task A.

2. The table shows the maximum and minimum suggested sizes for three different ages.

   Choose **one** of these ages and compare the maximum-sized and minimum-sized pitches.

   Hint: do it in the same way as you did for the seniors.

3. Try to find out the size of the football pitches in your school.

   You could do this by measuring them.

   How do they compare with the suggested sizes in the table?

4. The council are going to provide a football pitch near where you live for the community to use. Recommend a size and give a reason for your answer.

Rory Delap
Stoke City – midfield

Interesting fact:

The Premier League has its own regulations about pitch sizes.

When Stoke City were promoted to the Premier League in 2008, they opted to use the smallest size pitch allowed. Some people say they might have done this to help their player Rory Delap, who has one of the longest throw-ins in football.

9 Number: Ratio and proportion

9.1 Ratio

In this section you will learn how to:
- simplify a ratio
- divide a quantity in a given ratio.

Key words
ratio
proportion

WORKED EXAMPLE

In a keep fit class, the ratio of women to men is 3 : 2.

There are 24 women.

How many people are in the class?

<u>Solution</u>

There are 3 women for every 2 men. ———————→ That is what the ratio 3 : 2 means

Think of it like this:

WWW MM WWW MM WWW MM ....

How many groups of 3 women?

24 ÷ 3 = 8 groups ———————→ There are 24 women

So there are 8 × 2 = 16 men
and altogether there are 24 + 16 = 40 people.

We can check that is correct:

The ratio of women to men is 24 : 16 ———————→ We can divide both of these by 8

and that cancels to 3 : 2.

EXERCISE 9A

1 In a dance class there are two boys for every girl. There are 8 girls. How many boys are there?

FM Functional Maths **AU** (AO2) Assessing Understanding **PS** (AO3) Problem Solving

2 A mixed hockey team has seven women and four men.

   a What is the ratio of women to men? _____

   b What is the ratio of men to women? _____

3 A class has 20 girls and 10 boys. Write the ratio of girls to boys as simply as possible.

_____

4 Between us, we own 12 cats and four dogs. Complete these sentences.

   a There are _____ cats for every dog.

   Hint: complete
   cats : dogs = ___ : ___.

   b The ratio of cats to dogs can be written as _____ : 1.

5 Write these ratios as simply as possible. The first one has been done for you.

   a 8 : 4 = 2 : 1   **Hint:** we can divide both numbers by 4.

   b 9 : 3 = _____   **c** 20 : 5 = _____   **d** 6 : 8 = _____

   e 18 : 12 = _____   **f** 10 : 25 = _____   **g** 16 : 24 = _____

6 In a weather survey, the ratio of wet days to dry days is 3 : 1.

   Hint: complete
   wet : dry = ___ : ___.

   a There were five dry days. How many days were wet?

_____

   b How many days were in the survey altogether? _____

   c What **fraction** of the days were dry? Write your answer as simply as possible.

_____

AU 7 For most people, what are the ratios?

   a Noses to toes. _____   **b** Fingers to thumbs. _____

AU 8 The ratio of cows to sheep in a field is 3 : 2.

Say whether these statements are true or false.

a There are more cows than sheep. _____ **b** Over half the animals are sheep. _____

c The ratio of legs to animals is 4 : 1. _____ **d** 3 animals out of 5 are cows. _____

9 Bricks in a wall can be [   ] headers or [   ] stretchers.

Here is a row of bricks.

a What is the ratio of headers to stretchers in this row of bricks? _____

b What **fraction** of the bricks are headers? _____

Extension

1 The ratio of tulips to daffodils in a vase of flowers is 1 : 3.

There are 20 flowers altogether.

a How many of each sort are there?   Tulips _____   Daffodils _____

b What **fraction** are tulips? _____

2 A bowl of fruit has 12 apples and six pears.

a What is the ratio of apples to pears? Write your answer as simply as possible. _____

b What **fraction** of the fruit are apples? _____

3 A box contains only red pencils and blue pencils.
The ratio of the number of red pencils to the number of blue pencils is 2 : 3

What fraction of pencils are red? _____   (Total 2 marks)

Edexcel, November 2008, Paper 13 Foundation, Question 3

4 The ratio of students to teachers in a school is 14 : 1.

There are 868 pupils in the school. How many teachers are there? _____

9.2 Speed

In this section you will learn how to:
- make calculations about speed.

Key words
distance
kilometres per hour (km/h)
miles per hour (mph)
speed

WORKED EXAMPLE

Mr Wheeler drove for 2 hours at an average speed of 35 miles per hour (mph) and then for 3 hours at an average speed of 30 mph.

What was his average speed for the whole journey?

Solution

First we need to find the distance travelled.

2 hours at 35 mph is 2 × 35 = 70 miles.

3 hours at 30 mph is 3 × 30 = 90 miles.

Total distance = 70 + 90 = 160 miles.

Total time = 2 + 3 = 5 hours.

Average speed = 160 ÷ 5 = 32mph. ⟶ Remember: speed = $\frac{distance}{time}$

EXERCISE 9B

1. Geri cycles at an average speed of 12 mph. How far will she go in these times?

   a 1 hour _____   **b** 2 hours _____   **c** 5 hours _____

2. A racing cyclist can average 25 mph. How far will she travel in these times?

   a 2 hours _____   **b** 4 hours _____   **c** 6 hours _____

3. Sarah travelled for 2 hours at an average speed of 40 miles per hour.

   How far did she travel? _____ miles   (Total 2 marks)

   Edexcel, November 2008, Paper 13 Foundation, Question 3

4 30 mph is the speed limit in built-up areas.

Complete this table to show how far you can travel at that speed in different times.

Time (hours)	0.5	1	2	3	4
Distance (miles)		30			

5 A garden snail has been recorded as travelling at a speed of 17 cm per minute.

How far can it go in these times?

a 2 minutes _____   **b** 4 minutes _____   **c** 10 minutes _____

6 Adam cycled 24 km in 2 hours. Work out his average speed. _____ km/h

(Total 2 marks)

Edexcel, June 2008, Paper 10 Foundation, Question 8

7 Find the average speeds for these journeys by bicycle.

	Distance	Time	Average speed in miles per hour
a	14 miles	2 hours	
b	45 miles	3 hours	
c	48 miles	4 hours	

8 Bruce can walk at 4 mph.

a How far can he walk in 3 hours? _____ miles

b How long will he take to walk 20 miles? _____ hours

9 The speed limit on a motorway is 70 mph.

At that speed, how far can you drive in these times?

a 1 hour _____   **b** 3 hours _____

c $\frac{1}{2}$ hour _____   **d** $1\frac{1}{2}$ hours _____

10 The distance from Exeter to Carlisle is about 400 miles.

How long will that take at an average speed of 50 mph? _____

11 In France, Marie drives 120 kilometres in 2 hours.

What is her average speed in kilometres per hour (km/h)? _____

12 Karl cycles at an average speed of 24 km/h.

How far will he travel in these times?

a 1 hour _____ km   **b** 2 hours _____ km

c 30 minutes _____ km   **d** 15 minutes _____ km

Extension

1 Fran cycled from Norwich to Great Yarmouth in 2 hours and then back in 3 hours.
The route she chose was 30 miles each way.

a What was her average speed for each part of the journey?

Going: _____   Coming back: _____

b What was her average speed for the whole journey?

_____   **Hint:** you need to know the total distance and the total time.

2 Helga cycled 45 km in 2 hours and 30 minutes.

What was her average speed in km/h?

_____

9.3 Using ratios in different contexts

In this section you will learn how to:	**Key words**
● use the idea of ratio in different contexts.	exchange rate ratio speed

EXERCISE 9C

1 Find the ratios of the weights of these ingredients.

Write your answers as simply as possible.

a butter to flour: _____

b chocolate to cocoa: _____

c sugar to flour: _____

d flour to cocoa: _____

Recipe for Brownies	
Butter	90 g
Chocolate	120 g
Flour	30 g
Cocoa	20 g
Sugar	150 g
Eggs	2

Makes 8 brownies

FM 2 Write down the amount of each ingredient you will need to make 16 brownies.

Butter: _____ g   Chocolate: _____ g   Flour: _____ g

Cocoa: _____ g   Sugar: _____ g   Eggs: _____

FM 3 Max only has 3 eggs. How many brownies can he make? _____

4 How much butter would you need for 24 brownies? _____

FM 5 The exchange rate is 1.45 dollars to the pound.

Hint: this means that with £1 you can buy 1.45 dollars – that is, 1 dollar and 45 cents.

a How many dollars can you buy for £10 ? _____

b How many dollars can you buy for £200 ? _____

Hint: you will need to do a division. Use a calculator!

c How many pounds can you get for 500 dollars ? _____

AU 6 5 miles is approximately the same as 8 kilometres.

a How many kilometres are 10 miles ? _____

b How many kilometres are 20 miles ? _____

c How many miles are 24 kilometres ? _____

d Fill in the gaps in this table.

miles	5	50		100	200	
kilometres	8		96			400

e Erin said that a mile is more than 1 kilometre but less than 2 kilometres. Do you agree? Explain your answer.

_____

f The circumference of the Earth is about 25 000 miles. What is that in kilometres? Circle the correct answer from this list.

400 km   4 000 km   40 000 km   400 000 km   4 000 000 km

Extension

FM 1 A cereal comes in two pack sizes:
A small (200 g) pack costs £1.88
A large (300 g) pack costs £2.55

a What is the cost of 100 g in the **small** pack?

_____

b What is the cost of 100 g in the **large** pack?

_____

c Which size is better value? _____

FM **2** Which of these is better value?

A 200 ml bottle of shower gel for £2.40
A 300 ml bottle of shower gel for £3.99

Show how you decided.

FM **3** Which is better value?

Hint: by comparing the price of 200 g.

400 g of cheese for £3.40
600 g of cheese for £4.74

Give a reason for your answer.

checklist

☐ I can simplify a ratio.

☐ I can divide a quantity in a given ratio.

☐ I can make calculations about speed.

☐ I can use the idea of ratio in different contexts.

You have invited three friends around for dinner and chosen recipes for a starter, a main course and a dessert which you would like to cook for them. However, the recipe ingredients are not written for four people. Re-write them for four people.

Getting started

Here are some things to bear in mind.

- You should round off quantities sensibly if necessary. For example, you might want $\frac{1}{2}$ of 85 g which is 42.5 g but that would be silly in a recipe. 40 g or 45 g would be better.

- Sometimes you may need to adjust things. For example, you cannot include fractions of an egg. However, they do come in different sizes.

- Recipes can be flexible. A little bit more or less of an ingredient will not usually make much difference.

Starter

Indian potato cakes

Serves 8

650 g potatoes
40 g plain flour
115 g peas
115 g carrots
1 onion
1 red chilli
1 clove of garlic
1 teaspoon of cinnamon
1 teaspoon of cumin
Juice of $\frac{1}{2}$ a large lime
2 tablespoons of chopped coriander leaves
Salt and oil

Main
Aubergine meat balls
Serves 6

900 g aubergines
2 onions
450 g minced lamb
50 g grated Parmesan cheese
2 large eggs
Salt and pepper

Dessert
Apple and cinnamon pancakes
Serves 3

60 g plain flour
30 g wholemeal flour
1 large egg
150 ml of milk and water mixed
$\frac{1}{4}$ teaspoon of vanilla essence
$\frac{1}{2}$ teaspoon of ground cinnamon
2 small Cox's apples
3 tablespoons of dry cider

10 Algebra: Equations

10.1 Missing numbers

In this section you will learn how to:
- find a missing number in different situations
- form equations.

Key words
equation
expression

WORKED EXAMPLE

If $R = 8$, is it true that $4R - 8 = 2(R + 4)$?

Solution

Work out each side of the equation separately.

Left hand side:

$R = 8$

$4R = 32$ ─────────────────→ Remember $4R$ means $4 \times R$

$4R - 8 = 24$ ─────────────────→ because $32 - 8 = 24$

Right hand side:

$R = 8$

$R + 4 = 12$ ─────────────────→ Work out the bracket first

$2(R + 4) = 24$

Yes, it **is** true because both sides are 24.

EXERCISE 10A

Use a calculator in this exercise if you want to.

1 Fill in the missing numbers.

Hint: find $50 - 37$.

a _____ $+ 20 = 30$ **b** _____ $+ 37 = 50$ **c** _____ $+ 90 = 100$

d $42 + \underline{\hspace{1.5cm}} = 60$ **e** $\underline{\hspace{1.5cm}} + 25 = 70$ **f** $38 + \underline{\hspace{1.5cm}} = 63$

2 Fill in the missing numbers in these questions.

a $\underline{\hspace{1.5cm}} - 7 = 10$ **b** $\underline{\hspace{1.5cm}} - 12 = 8$ **c** $\underline{\hspace{1.5cm}} - 20 = 10$

Hint: the answer is <u>not</u> 3.   **Hint:** do an <u>addition</u> to answer this.

d $\underline{\hspace{1.5cm}} - 32 = 8$ **e** $\underline{\hspace{1.5cm}} - 7 = 44$ **f** $\underline{\hspace{1.5cm}} - 34 = 26$

3 Fill in the missing numbers in these multiplications.

a $\underline{\hspace{1.5cm}} \times 2 = 12$ **b** $\underline{\hspace{1.5cm}} \times 3 = 33$ **c** $\underline{\hspace{1.5cm}} \times 4 = 100$

4 Fill in the missing numbers here.

a $\underline{\hspace{1.5cm}} \div 2 = 8$ **b** $\underline{\hspace{1.5cm}} \div 2 = 25$ **c** $\underline{\hspace{1.5cm}} \div 4 = 20$

Hint: the answer is <u>not</u> 4.   **Hint:** do a <u>multiplication</u> to answer this.

d $\underline{\hspace{1.5cm}} \div 10 = 3$ **e** $\frac{1}{2}$ of $\underline{\hspace{1.5cm}} = 12$ **f** $\frac{1}{4}$ of $\underline{\hspace{1.5cm}} = 20$

Hint: the answer is <u>not</u> 6.

5 Julian bought 6 cartons of juice and the cost was £2.70.

How much was each carton? $\underline{\hspace{3cm}}$

PS 6 Laxmi bought 5 oranges. She received 30p change from a £2 coin.

How much was each orange? $\underline{\hspace{3cm}}$

7 James bought 6 cinema tickets. He paid £38.10. Each ticket was the same price.

Work out the price of each cinema ticket. $\underline{\hspace{3cm}}$

(Total 2 marks)

Edexcel, March 2008, Paper 10 Section A Foundation, Question 8

8 $N = 12$. Complete the following equations.

a $N + 23 =$ _____

b $N - 9 =$ _____

c $4N =$ _____

d $\frac{1}{2}N =$ _____

e $2N + 3 =$ _____

f $5N - 20 =$ _____

9 Complete these equations.

a

$F = 6$

$2F =$ _____

$2F + 8 =$ _____

b

$G = 9$

$G + 1 =$ _____

$3(G + 1) =$ _____

c

$H =$ _____

$2H = 14$

$2H - 8 =$ _____

d

$K = 3.5$

$3K =$ _____

$3K + 4.5 =$ _____

Extension

1 $Y = 14$. Fill in the missing **numbers** in these equations.

a $Y +$ _____ $= 17$

Hint: remember, Y is 14.

b $2Y +$ _____ $= 33$

c $2Y -$ _____ $= 20$

2 Work with a partner to complete these equations.

a

$t = -4$

$2t =$ _____

$2t + 3 =$ _____

b

$k = -5$

$4k =$ _____

$4k + 6 =$ _____

c $V = -3$ **d** $g = -2$

$3V =$ _____ $6g =$ _____

$3V - 4 =$ _____ $6g - 3 =$ _____

10.2 Solving equations

In this section you will learn how to:
- solve different types of equations.

Key words

equation
expression
solution
solve

WORKED EXAMPLE

Solve the equation $4d - 23 = 25$.

__Solution__

First **add** 23 to both sides of the equation.

$4d - 23 + 23 = 25 + 23$

$\qquad 4d = 48$ ⟶ This leaves $4d$ on its own.

Now divide both sides by 4.

$\qquad d = 12$ ⟶ This is the solution to the equation.

EXERCISE 10B

You can use a calculator for these questions.

1 Solve these equations.

Hint: find the answers by subtraction.

a $x + 5 = 20$ $x =$ _____   **b** $y + 12 = 19$ $y =$ _____

2 Solve these equations. | **Hint:** the answer to **a** is <u>not</u> 3.

a $g - 4 = 7$ $g =$ _____ **b** $r - 2.3 = 4.4$ $r =$ _____

3 Solve these equations.

a $2t = 8$ $t =$ _____ **b** $4y = 24$ $y =$ _____

4 Solve these equations. **Hint:** find each answer by doing a multiplication.

a $\frac{1}{2}p = 3$ $p =$ _____ **b** $\frac{T}{2} = 9$ $T =$ _____

5 Complete the solutions to these equations.

a $3y + 5 = 17$

$3y =$ _____

Check: does $3 \times$ (your answer) $+ 5$ make 17?

$y =$ _____

b $4x - 3 = 29$ **c** $5w + 12 = 47$

$4x =$ _____ $5w =$ _____

$x =$ _____ $w =$ _____

d $12g - 32 = 16$ **e** $\frac{m}{3} - 8 = 2$

$12g =$ _____ $\frac{m}{3} =$ _____

$g =$ _____ $m =$ _____

6 Solve these equations.

Look at the previous questions if you need help.

a $2r + 5 = 13$

b $3k - 14 = 16$

c $12y + 92 = 200$

d $20 + 5n = 100$

7 Solve these equations.

a Solve $2x = 12$ (1)

b Solve $c - 8 = 11$ (1)

c Solve $\dfrac{y}{5} = 2$ (1)

(Total 3 marks)

Edexcel, June 2008, Paper 13 Foundation, Question 7

Extension

1 The solution to an equation could be a negative number or a decimal.

Try these.

a $y + 6 = 2$

> **Hint:** what is 2 − 6?

b $k + 10 = 3$

c $3y = -15$

d $10T = 36$

e $4h + 2 = 12$

f $2y - 5 = 16$

10.3 Using equations

In this section you will learn how to:
● form and solve equations in different contexts.

Key words
expression
equation
solution
solve

EXERCISE 10C

1 Clark buys two tins of paint. He pays with a £20 note. He is left with £4. How much is each tin of paint? We could write:

$$2 \times \text{cost of a tin of paint} + 4 = 20$$

or $$2C + 4 = 20$$

where C stands for the cost of a tin of paint.

Solve the equation $2C + 4 = 20$.

_____

_____

2 Lois buys two DVDs. She has £8 change from a £20 note.

a Turn this story into an equation. Use C for the cost of one DVD.

_____

b Solve the equation.

_____

_____

_____

AU 3 Make up a story for this equation.

$$5C + 10 = 100$$

_____

_____

4 Jimmy thinks of a number. Call it N.

He multiplies it by 4 and adds 6.

a Complete this expression for the result. $4N +$ _____

b If the result is 18, write down an equation. _____

c Solve the equation. _____

_____

$$N = \underline{\hspace{2cm}}$$

5 Kara thinks of a number. Call it N.

She multiplies it by 5 and subtracts 12.

a Write an expression for the result.   _____

b The answer she gets is 53. Write down an equation. _____

c Solve the equation. _____

_____

_____

6 Make up a 'think of a number' story for this equation: $2N + 20 = 32$

_____

_____

Extension

PS 1 In the USA, people often use the Fahrenheit (F) scale instead of Celsius (C) to measure temperature.

Here is a formula to change Celsius into Fahrenheit.

$$1.8C + 32 = F$$

a Complete this table. Use the formula to help you. Choose your own numbers for the last two columns.

Hint: for example, if C is 10 then $F = 1.8 \times 10 + 32 = 50$.

Degrees C	10	20	30	40		
Degrees F	50					

b If F is 212, then we can write an equation: $1.8C + 32 = 212$

Solve this equation. ——————————————————

——————————————————

——————————————————

c What temperature, in degrees C, is the same as 140 degrees F? ——————

d What temperature, in degrees C, is the same as 302 degrees F? ——————

checklist

☐ I can find a missing number in different situations.

☐ I can form equations.

☐ I can solve different types of equations.

☐ I can form and solve equations in different contexts.

You could work with a partner on this task.

George is organising a coach trip from his local community centre.

A 50-seater coach will cost £100 in total to hire.

He plans to make these charges for the trip:

Adults	£5
Children	£1

He wants to make sure that he will cover his costs and not make a loss.

Task A

1. If only adults go on the trip, how many are needed to cover the cost?

2. Explain why the trip will make a loss if only children go on the trip.

3. Suppose there are 14 adults on the trip. How many children must there be to cover the cost of the coach?

4. Suppose there are nine children on the trip. How many adults must there be to cover the cost?

5. Suppose there are five adults and the rest of the seats are taken by children. What is the profit or loss?

6. George has asked for your advice. He thinks there will be roughly equal numbers of adults and children. Can you tell him how many tickets he needs to sell to cover his costs?

Now George has been asked to lower the cost for Senior Citizens.

He now has three prices for tickets:

Adults (full price)	£5
Senior Citizens	£3
Children	£1

Task B

1 If only senior citizens go on the trip, how many must there be to cover the cost of the coach?

2 George still thinks that roughly half the tickets will be for children. He thinks that the rest will split roughly equally between full-price adults and senior citizens. What is your advice now about how many tickets he needs to sell?

11 Algebra: Number sequences and patterns

11.1 Sequences of numbers

In this section you will learn how to:
- identify patterns in number sequences and extend them.

Key words
pattern
sequence

WORKED EXAMPLE

Here is a simple sequence of numbers.

1   2   4   7   11   16

What are the next two numbers?

Solution

Look at the **differences** between the numbers.

Numbers: 1   2   4   7   11   16   _____   _____

Differences: 1   2   3   4   5   _____   _____

The next differences will be 6 and 7.

So the next two numbers are 16 + 6 = **22** and 22 + 7 = **29**.

EXERCISE 11A

1 Find the next number in these sequences.

a 8, 10, 12, 14, _____

b 7, 10, 13, 16, _____

c 10, 14, 18, 22, _____

d 21, 19, 17, 15, _____

e 31, 34, 37, 40, _____

f 67, 72, 77, 82, _____

2 **a** What are the next two numbers?

   12   15   18   21   _____   _____

   b Explain how you did it.

   _____

3 Fill in the missing numbers in these sequences.

   a 15, 19, 23, _____ , 31, 35   **b** 44, 48, _____ , 56, 60

   c 70, 67, _____ , 61, 58   **d** 22, _____ , 30, 34, 38

   e 50, _____ , 62, 68, 74   **f** 42, 33, _____ , 15, 6

4 Find the next number in these sequences.

   a 2, 4, 8, 16, _____   **b** 3, 6, 12, 24, _____

   c Write down a similar sequence starting with 5. _____

5 Follow the pattern. There is no need for a calculator.

   a $3 \times 4 = 12$ **b** $2 \times 7 = 14$ **c** $7 \times 6 = 42$

   $33 \times 4 = 132$ $22 \times 7 = 154$ $77 \times 6 = 462$

   $333 \times 4 = 1332$ $222 \times 7 = 1554$ $777 \times 6 = 4662$

   $3333 \times 4 =$ _____ $2222 \times 7 =$ _____ $7777 \times 6 =$ _____

6 Here are the first five terms of a simple sequence.

   23   19   15   11   7

   a Write down the next term of the sequence. _____   (1)

   b Explain how you found your answer.

   _____

   _____   (1)

   (Total 2 marks)

   Edexcel, June 2008, Paper 10 Section B, Question 4

7 Here are the first five terms of a simple sequence.

4   7   10   13   16

a Write down the next two terms of the sequence.   _____ , _____   (2)

b Explain how you found your answer.

_____

_____   (1)

(Total 3 marks)

Edexcel, November 2007, Paper 10 Section A Foundation, Question 2

Extension

1 Find the next number in these sequences.

a 5   6   8   11   15   _____

b 20   21   23   26   30   _____

c 1   5   10   16   23   _____

Hint: look at the differences.

2 The rule for these sequences is 'double the last number and subtract 1'.

Write down the next two terms.

a 2   3   5   9   ____   ____   **b** 4   7   13   ____   ____

3 The rule for this sequence is 'add the last two numbers to get the next one'.

Find the next three numbers.

1   1   2   3   5   8   ____   ____   ____

4 Continue this pattern.

$$11 \times 11 = 121$$
$$111 \times 111 = 12321$$
$$1111 \times 1111 = 1234321$$

_____

11.2 Patterns and numbers

In this section you will learn how to:
- extend patterns and link them to sequences of numbers.

Key words
pattern
sequence

WORKED EXAMPLE

Look at this sequence of hexagons.

The second picture is made from 11 lines.

If the sequence continues, how many lines will there be in the 7th picture?

Solution

Count the lines in each picture.

The number of lines goes up by 5 each time.

Picture	1st	2nd	3rd
Lines	6	11	16

The sequence will continue: 21   26   31   36

The 7th picture will have 36 lines.

EXERCISE 11B

1 Look at this sequence of 'words'.

OXO   OXOXO   OXOXOXO

a Write down the next word in the sequence. _____

b List the number of letters in each 'word'. _____

c How many letters will there be in the 5th 'word'? _____

2 Here is a sequence of patterns.

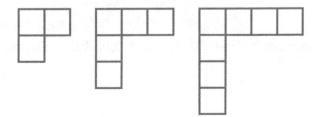

a Write down the number of squares in each of these patterns.

_____

b Draw the next pattern in the sequence.

Hint: draw it if you need to.

c How many squares are there in the 5th pattern? _____

3 These patterns of squares are made from dots and lines.

a Draw the next pattern.

b Fill in this table.

Squares	1	2	3	4
Dots	4			
Lines	4			

c How many dots and lines will there be in the next pattern?

Dots: _____   Lines: _____

4 Here are some patterns made up of dots.

Pattern number 1   Pattern number 2   Pattern number 3

a Draw pattern number 4 next to pattern number 3.   (1)

b Complete the table for Pattern number 4 and Pattern number 5.   (1)

Pattern number	1	2	3	4	5
Number of dots	1	4	7		

(Total 2 marks)

Edexcel, March 2007, Paper 10 Section A Foundation, Question 2

5 The first even number is 2.

a Write down the 3rd even number.   _____   (1)

Here are some patterns made from sticks.

Pattern number 1   Pattern number 2   Pattern number 3

b Complete Pattern number 4.

Pattern number 4

(1)

c Complete the table.

Pattern number	1	2	3	4	5
Number of sticks	3	6	9		

(2)

(Total 3 marks)

Edexcel, June 2009, Paper 2 Foundation, Question 5 a, b and c

Extension

1 Look at this sequence.

A   ABA   ABCBA   ABCDCBA

a Write in the next 'word' in the sequence. _____

b How many letters are there when B is in the middle? _____

c How many letters are there when C is in the middle? _____

d How many letters are there when D is in the middle? _____

e Imagine the sequence continues.
How many letters will there be when J is in the middle? _____

2 Work with a partner on this question.

Draw a set of increasing patterns of your own.

Write down any sequence of numbers that goes with it.

Find the number for the 10th pattern.

11.3 Patterns and numbers in action

In this section you will learn how to:
● identify patterns in everyday situations.

Key words

pattern

sequence

EXERCISE 11C

PS 1 Fences can be made from posts and bars.

These sections of fencing have two bars between each post.

The second one has 3 posts and 4 bars.

Fill in this table.

Posts	2	3	4	5
Bars		4		

PS 2 The docks in a seaside town are being renovated.

Bollards will be placed along the edge of the dock.

The bollards will be 3 metres apart.

This line of three bollards is 6 metres long.

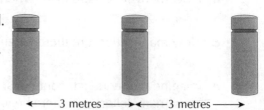

← 3 metres → ← 3 metres →

a How long will a line of four bollards be? _____ metres

b Complete this table.

Number of bollards	2	3	4	5
Length of line (metres)		6		

c How long will a line of 6 bollards be? _____

d A line of bollards is 24 metres long.

How many bollards are there? _____

FM 3 A furniture manufacturer makes bookcases out of MDF using standard components.

The number of shelves can vary. This is a three-shelf bookcase.

It has four horizontal pieces (including the top) and two side pieces.

It does not have a back to it.

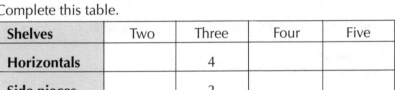

a Complete this table.

Shelves	Two	Three	Four	Five
Horizontals		4		
Side pieces		2		

b The manufacturer is planning to add a six-shelf bookcase to the range.

How many lengths of MDF will it require altogether? _____

Extension

1 In a car park the parking area is broken up by islands with plants in them.

Kerb stones are used around the islands. There are straight kerb stones and corner ones. The islands are all the same width but can be made in different lengths.

This is what they look like from above. Length 2 has 4 corner stones and 6 straights.

length 1   length 2

a Sketch an island of length 3 next to island 2.

b Copy and complete this table.

Length	1	2	3	4
Corner stones		4		
Straights		6		

c How many of each type will be needed for an island of length 6?

Corners: _____   Straights: _____

d The designer is considering the possibility of square islands instead of rectangular ones. Here is one example.

On a separate piece of paper, investigate the number of straight and corner kerbs needed for square islands.

FM 2 Kavita is tiling her bathroom wall.

At the corner of each tile she must put a small plastic spacer.

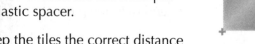

These keep the tiles the correct distance apart until the adhesive is dry.

One tile on its own needs four spacers. Three tiles in a row need eight spacers.

a Draw two tiles in a row and mark in the spacers.

How many spacers are needed? _____

b Complete this table.

Tiles in a row	1	2	3	4	5
Spacers needed					

c How many spacers are needed for 10 tiles in a row? _____

d Suppose you have two rows of tiles.

On a separate piece of paper, investigate the number of spacers you need for different lengths in this case.

FM **3** Paul is making a fence in his garden.

Each panel of the fence needs a post at each end.

For example, here is a four-panel fence made with five posts.

Posts cost £3.20 each and panels cost £14.80.

a How much does a four-panel fence cost?

£ _____ (3)

b Another fence costs a total of £111.20.

How many panels are there in this fence?

_____ (3)

(Total 6 marks)

June 2009, Paper 2 Foundation, Question 16

checklist

☐ I can identify patterns in number sequences and extend them.

☐ I can extend patterns and link them to sequences of numbers.

☐ I can identify patterns in everyday situations.

Problem Solving
Is there anybody out there?

Since 1985 the SETI Institute has been looking for signs of intelligent life in the universe. They employ about 150 scientists and support staff. You might like to look at their website.

One way to detect intelligent life is to look for electromagnetic signals from space that seem to have a regular repeating pattern and are not just random. (Mobile phone signals are one example of electromagnetic signals.)

We are used to digital information. It is at the heart of computers, mobile phones and all our digital technology.

Task A

A digital signal can be thought of as a string of 0s and 1s, these are called binary digits or bits for short.

Look at each of these digital signals.

Which ones do you think might have a repeating pattern?

a 11011011011011011…
b 00001100001100001100…
c 10101111010111101011110…
d 001010001010001010001010…
e 10110100101010101010010100010…
f 00100011001000110010001100…

Write down the repeating section, if there is one.

Task B

1 Here is a sequence of bits.

    100111001110011110011…

a This is a repeating sequence. What and how long is the repeating section?

b Check that the 1st, 6th and 11th bits are the same. What other bits must be the same as the first one?

c Imagine you start writing down the sequence, starting from the 20th bit. How will it continue? Will it be the same as the original sequence?

2 Here is a repeating sequence.

    0111011101110…

Say whether the following will be a 0 or a 1:

a The 10th bit   b The 20th bit   c The 30th bit

d Which bits will be 0s?

3 Here is a repeating signal. You have only been given the sixth bit.

    _ _ _ _ _ 1 _ _ _ _ _ _ _ _ _ …

You know that it repeats every four bits.

What could the first four bits be?

Try to find all the possible answers. How many are there?

Task C

1 In computing, 8 bits are called a **byte**. A piece of information, such as a letter or a pixel, can be stored as one or more bytes.

> 1 **Kilobyte** (KB) is 1000 bytes
>
> 1 **Megabyte** (MB) is a million bytes
>
> 1 **Gigabyte** (GB) is a billion bytes (1000 million)
>
> 1 **Terabyte** (TB) is a million million bytes

a How many bits are there in 1 Kilobyte?

b How many bits are there in 1 Megabyte?

2 This signal consists of one byte repeated continuously 001011000010…

a What is the repeating byte?

b What are the 50th, 70th and 100th bits?

3 A signal consists of one repeated byte.

Most of the signal has been lost but we do know the following.

The 2nd, 7th, 12th, 16th and 22nd bits are all 1s.

The 17th digit is 0.

What could the byte be? Find all the possible answers.

4 Can you make up your own 'lost digits' puzzle?

Give some clues that will help someone to work out the signal.

Did you know: half a byte is called a nibble!

12 Geometry: Volume

12.1 **Shapes made from cubes**

In this section you will learn how to:	Key words
• find the surface area and volume of shapes made from cubes.	centimetre cube cube surface area volume

WORKED EXAMPLE

Find the volume and surface area of this shape made from centimetre cubes.

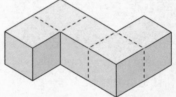

Solution

The shape is made from five centimetre cubes, so the volume is 5 cm^3.

The surface area is the total of the areas of each face.

The top has an area of 5 cm^2. ——————————→ Just count the squares.

The bottom is also 5 cm^2.

Around the edge there are 12 squares, ——————→ You can see 6 squares in the diagram
so the area is 12 cm^2. and another 6 are hidden.

The total surface area is 5 + 5 + 12 = 22 cm^2. ——————→ Make the shape from cubes if you are
not sure about this.

EXERCISE 12A

It will help if you have some cubes when you are working through this chapter.

You can clip them together to make the different shapes.

The diagrams in this section are not drawn to scale.

1 Here is a shape made out of centimetre cubes.

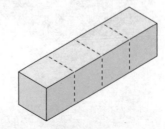

   a How long is it? _____ cm

b What is the volume? _____ cm^3

c The area of the top is 4 cm^2. What is the **total** area of all **six** faces? _____ cm^2

2 Here is a different arrangement of the cubes in question 1.

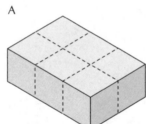

    a What is the volume? _____ cm^3

    b How many faces does it have? _____

    c What is the **total** area of **all** the faces? _____ cm^2

3 On a separate piece of paper, draw a different arrangement of four centimetre cubes and find the total surface area.

Surface area = _____ cm^2

4 Here are two different shapes made with six centimetre cubes.

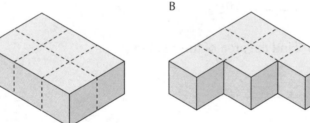

A   B

    a Find the volume and surface area of shapes A and B.

       A   Volume = _____ cm^3 Surface area = _____ cm^2

       B   Volume = _____ cm^3 Surface area = _____ cm^2

    b Find an arrangement of six cubes that has a larger surface area than shape B.

    Surface area = _____ cm^2

5 A strip of paper one centimetre wide is wrapped around the outside of this shape made from centimetre cubes.

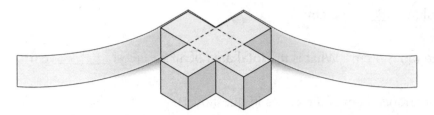

a How long is the strip of paper? _____cm

b What is the volume of the shape? _____ cm³

c What is the surface area of the shape? _____ cm²

6 A shaded shape has been drawn on the centimetre grid.

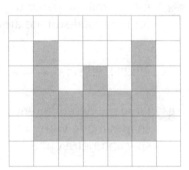

a Find the perimeter of the shaded shape.

_____ cm   (1)

b Find the area of the shaded shape.

_____ cm²   (1)

Here is a solid prism made from centimetre cubes.

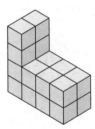

c Find the volume of this prism.

_____ cm³   (2)

(Total 4 marks)

Edexcel, June 2008, Paper 2 Foundation, Question 7

Extension

PS 1 Here are two different arrangements of eight cubes.

A   B

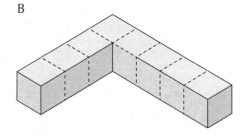

a Find the volume and surface area of each.

A   Volume = _____ cm^3 Surface area = _____ cm^2

B   Volume = _____ cm^3 Surface area = _____ cm^2

b Make some other shapes with eight cubes.

What different surface areas can you find?

_____

2 Salim says that if you put several cubes together, the surface area will always be an even number. Try some arrangements of **five** cubes to see if you agree with him. Write down the surface areas you find.

_____

12.2 Cuboids

In this section you will learn how to:
● find the volume and surface area of a cuboid.

Key words
cuboid
surface area
volume

WORKED EXAMPLE

Calculate the volume and the surface area of this box.

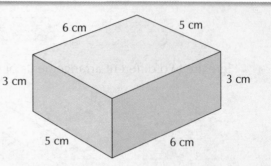

Solution

The box is a cuboid.

Volume = length × width × height
= 6 × 5 × 3 = 90 cm³.

To find the surface area, we need to find the area of each of the six faces and add them together.

The area of the top and the bottom = 6 × 5 = 30 cm².

The area of the front and the back = 6 × 3 = 18 cm².

The area of each side = 5 × 3 = 15 cm².

Total surface area = 2 × 30 + 2 × 18 + 2 × 15 = 126 cm². → Notice that there are three identical pairs of faces.

EXERCISE 12B

1 Find the volumes of these cuboids. They are made from one-centimetre cubes.

a

b

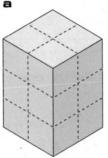
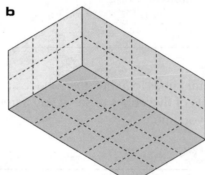

a Volume = _____ cm³

b Volume = _____ cm³

2 Find the volumes of these cuboids. All the lengths are in centimetres.

a

b

c

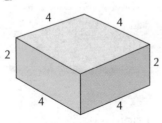
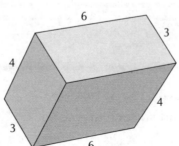
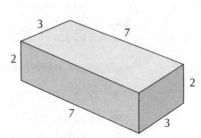

a _____ cm³

b _____ cm³

c _____ cm³

3 Here is the net of a box. The lengths are in centimetres.

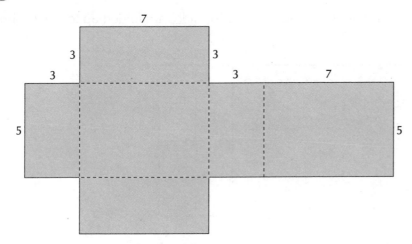

Hint: find the area of the net.

a What is the surface area of the box? _____ cm^2

b What are the length, width and height of the box?

_____

c What is the volume of the box? _____ cm^3

4 Find the surface area of each of the cuboids in question 1.
Show how you find the answer each time.

a _____ cm^2 Reason _____

b _____ cm^2 Reason _____

5 For large spaces, cubic centimetres are too small and it is more sensible to use cubic
metres (m^3).

The floor of a rectangular room is 5 m long and 4 m wide. The height of the room is 2.5 m.

a What is the area of the floor? _____ m^2

b What is the volume of the room? _____ m^3

153

6 A square piece of paper has sides 10 cm long.

A two-centimetre square is cut out of each corner. The sides are folded up to make a box without a lid.

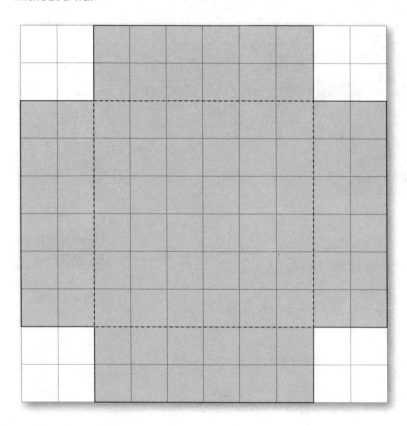

a What is the volume of the box? _____ cm^3

b Investigate what the volume would be if a **different-sized square** were cut off each corner.

_____

_____

_____

7 A cuboid has

    a length of 10 cm,
    a width of 5 cm,
    a height of 3 cm.

Work out the volume of the cuboid.

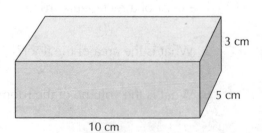

_____ cm^3

(Total 2 marks)

Edexcel, March 2007, Paper 10 Foundation, Question 5

Extension

AU 1 A cuboid has sides of 2 cm, 2 cm and 15 cm.

  a Show that the volume is 60 cm^3.

  _____

  _____

  b Find the lengths of the sides of some other cuboids that have the same volume of 60 cm^3.

  _____

  _____

12.3 Cuboids in real situations

In this section you will learn how to:
● find the volume and surface area of cuboids in real situations.

Key words
cuboid
litre
surface area
volume

EXERCISE 12C

PS 1 Stock cubes are used in cooking to add flavour to stews. You buy them in a box.

Each stock cube is 3 cm long, 2 cm wide and 1.2 cm high.

The box is 10 cm long, 6 cm wide and 1.2 cm high.

How many cubes will fit in the box? _____

FM 2 A builder is putting down a concrete floor for an extension to a house.

The floor of the extension measures 4 m by 3 m.

A hole has been dug which is 0.5 m deep.

What volume of concrete must he mix to fill the hole? _____ m^3

FM 3 A small swimming pool is 10 m long, 6 m wide and 2 m deep.

a What is the volume of the pool? _____ m^3

b How many **litres** of water are needed to fill the pool? _____ litres

Hint: there are 1000 litres in 1 cubic metre.

Extension

AU 1 A large matchbox is 12 cm long, 7 cm wide and 2.5 cm high.
On the box it says, 'Average contents: 220 matches'.

a What is the volume of the box? _____ cm^3

b Explain why the volume of one match must be less than one cubic centimetre.

_____

The box has a cardboard sleeve
with a tray inside.

c What is the area of cardboard used to make the sleeve? Explain how you calculated this.

_____

d What is the area of cardboard used to make the tray? Explain how you calculated this.

_____

e Why might your answers to parts c and d not be accurate?

_____

_____

2 Carly's office is 10 m long, 7 m wide and 3 m high.

AU

FM **a** What is the total area of the walls, ignoring any windows or doors? _____ m^2

b The walls are going to be repainted. One tin of paint is enough for 20 m^2. The walls will need two coats of paint. How many tins will be required? Explain how you found your answer.

_____

_____

Regulations say that there must be at least 11 m^3 of space for every person working in an office.

c What is the volume of Carly's office? _____ m^3

d 15 people work in Carly's office. Show whether this breaks the rules or not.

_____

_____

e New carpet is being laid in the office. It costs £16.49 per square metre.

What is the total cost of the new carpet? _____

You could work with a partner on this activity.

Useful facts:

Quantities of liquids are often given in litres (l) or millilitres (ml).

1 litre = 1000 ml

1 litre fills a volume of 1000 cm³.

Imagine a cube where each edge is 10 cm long. That will hold 1 litre of liquid.

Task A

A supermarket sells its own brand orange juice in two different cartons.

- The **large** carton is 7.5 cm wide, 7 cm deep and 20 cm high. It holds 1 litre.
- The **small** carton is 5 cm wide, 4 cm deep and 11 cm high. It holds 200 ml.

1 Show that the large carton can hold 1 litre of juice.

2 Show that the small carton can hold 200 ml.

The supermarket is interested in the amount of packaging used for the cartons. The manager has asked for your help.

The manager thinks that because the large carton can hold five times as much juice as the small carton, it must need five times as much cardboard to make.

3 What evidence can you give the manager to support his theory or to show that it is incorrect?

Task B

The supermarket plans to start selling the small cartons in a six-pack.

In this pack, six small cartons are held together by transparent plastic film in the shape of a cuboid. This can be done in different ways.

1 The manager has asked you to investigate the different possible arrangements of small cartons in a six-pack.

   How many can you find? Make a sketch of each one to show the manager.

The manager thinks that all the arrangements will use the same amount of transparent plastic film to hold them together because they each contain six cartons.

2 What evidence can you give the manager to support his theory or to show that he is incorrect?

Task C

The manager has asked you to recommend the best way to arrange the cartons in the six-pack. You should take these factors into account.

- The space they will take up on the shelves
- The ease with which they will stack on top of one another without falling over
- The amount of transparent plastic film needed to hold them together
- The visual impact they will have on a customer
- The ease with which they can be carried in a shopping bag

What is your recommendation and what are the reasons for your choice?

13 Geometry: Circles

Drawing circles

In this section you will learn how to:
- draw circles and use vocabulary connected with them.

Key words

arc
chord
diameter
perpendicular
radius

sector
tangent

WORKED EXAMPLE

Draw a tangent to this circle at the point P.

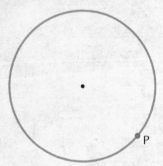

Solution

Start by drawing a **diameter** from P. This will go through the centre of the circle.

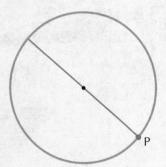

The tangent is **perpendicular** to the diameter. ⟶ Perpendicular means 'at a right angle'.

FM Functional Maths   **AU** (AO2) Assessing Understanding   **PS** (AO3) Problem Solving

Use a protractor to measure 90 degrees.

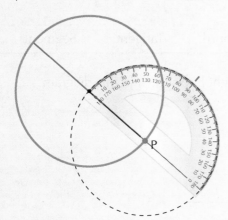

Then draw in the tangent.

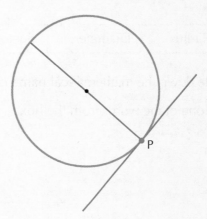

EXERCISE 13A

 a Measure the radius of each of these circles.

radius of A = _____

radius of B = _____

radius of C = _____

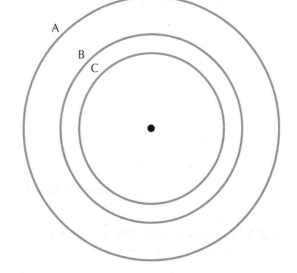

b Draw a circle of radius 3 cm on the diagram and label it D.

c What are the diameters of the four circles?

diameter of A = _____

diameter of B = _____

diameter of C = _____

diameter of D = _____

2 Here are some words which describe parts of a circle.

| Radius | Diameter | Sector | Chord | Tangent | Segment |

a Write down the mathematical name of the straight line shown in this diagram.

Use one of the words from the box.

_____ (1)

b Write down the mathematical name of the straight line shown in the diagram.

Use one of the words from the box.

_____ (1)

(Total 2 marks)

Edexcel, March 2009, Paper 9 Foundation, Unit 2 Stage 2, Question 4

3 Fill in the gaps in these sentences.
Choose from these words:

centre, radius, tangent, diameter, chord, radius

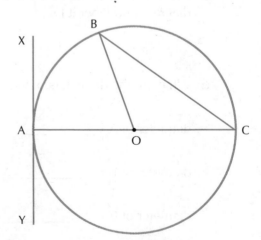

a AC is a _____

b OB is a _____

c XY is a _____

d OA is a _____

e BC is a _____

f O is the _____

4 Here are 5 diagrams and 5 labels.
In each diagram the centre of the circle is marked with a cross (X).

Match each diagram to its label. One has been done for you.

Diagram　　　　　　　　　　　　　　**Label**

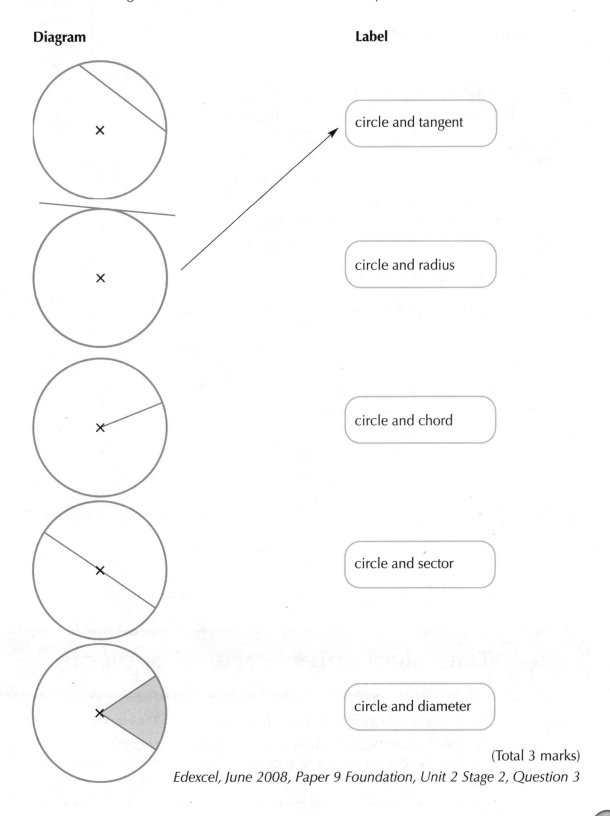

circle and tangent

circle and radius

circle and chord

circle and sector

circle and diameter

(Total 3 marks)

Edexcel, June 2008, Paper 9 Foundation, Unit 2 Stage 2, Question 3

5 Each side of this square is 6 cm.

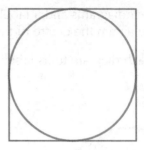

Diagram not accurately drawn

a What is the diameter of the circle? _____

b What is the radius of the circle? _____

6 A semicircle is **half** of a circle. On a separate sheet of paper, draw a semicircle with a diameter 8 cm long.

Extension

PS 1 This star is made by drawing four quarter circles.

See if you can draw one.

Use the dots on this grid to help you.

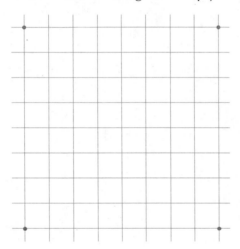

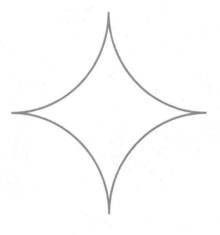

13.2 The circumference of a circle

In this section you will learn how to:
● use the connection between the diameter and the circumference of a circle.

Key words
circle
diameter
radius

WORKED EXAMPLE

A bicycle wheel has a diameter of 70 cm. How could we measure the circumference?
What does the circumference tell you?

<u>Solution</u>

The circumference is the distance all round the rim. Measuring this is difficult.
You can find it by wheeling the bike in a straight line.

Start with the valve at the bottom and stop when it
gets to the bottom again. Mark the start and finish
points on the ground.

Measure the distance between the two points.

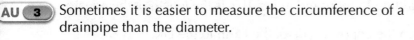

circumference

You will find that the circumference is about 220 cm for a wheel that size.

It tells you how far the bike moves forward when the wheel goes round once.

EXERCISE 13B

You can use this graph to find the circumference
of a circle, approximately.

1 Use the graph to find the circumference of a circle
with a diameter of:

a 10 cm _____   **b** 5 mm _____   **c** 8 m _____

d 10 km _____   **e** 6 mm _____   **f** 7 m _____

2 Use the graph to find the circumference of a circle with
a **radius** of:

a 3 cm _____   **b** 4.5 m _____   **c** 2 cm _____

Hint: find the diameter first.

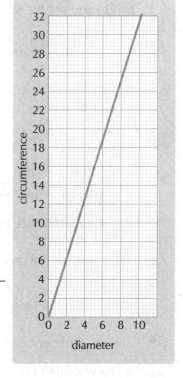

AU **3** Sometimes it is easier to measure the circumference of a
drainpipe than the diameter.

The circumference of a pipe is 20 cm.

Hint: use the graph.

a What is the diameter? _____

b On a separate sheet of paper, draw a circle with a circumference of 20 cm.

c Why might it be hard to measure the diameter of a drainpipe? _____

_____

4 A park has a circular flower bed with a circumference of 14 m.

What is the diameter? _____

Extension

1 Over 2000 years ago, Archimedes proved that the circumference of any circle is approximately $3\frac{1}{7}$ × the diameter.

    a Use a calculator to find the circumference of a circle with a diameter of 10 cm by doing the multiplication $3\frac{1}{7}$ × 10. _____

    b Do you get the same answer from the graph on the previous page? _____

2 A circle with a diameter of 10 metres has a circumference of approximately 31.4 metres.

    a Explain why a circle with a diameter of 20 metres must have a circumference of approximately 62.8 metres.

_____

    b Complete this table:

Diameter (metres)	5	10	20	40
Circumference (metres)		31.4		

3 The graph on the previous page also works for spheres.

The diameter of a tennis ball is 10 cm.
What is the circumference of a tennis ball? _____

4 The circumference of the Earth is 25 thousand miles. This is the length of the equator.

FM
AU
    a New Zealand is almost on the opposite side of the Earth to the UK. If you could travel there by the shortest route, how far would you go? _____

    b What is the diameter of the Earth? _____

13.3 Circles in action

In this section you will learn how to:
● handle circles in realistic situations.

Key words
circumference
diameter
radius

EXERCISE 13C

FM 1 Measure the diameters of some circular coins.

a Record your results.

Value	1p	2p	5p	10p	£1	£2
Diameter						

b Is it true that larger coins have a bigger value? Give a reason for your answer.

_____

2 This is a simple version of the flower of life, a symbol that is found in many cultures.

Draw it here.

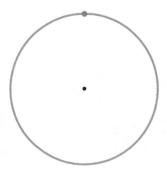

Hint: start with an arc using the point marked as the centre and the same radius as the circle.

FM 3 Drink cans could be packed together in two different ways.

These diagrams show an overhead view.

Square packing   Hexagonal packing

a Which type is commonly used in packs of drinks cans? _____

b Draw around a coin to illustrate square packing of six cans arranged in a rectangle.

c Now draw round a coin to illustrate hexagonal packing of seven cans arranged in a hexagon.

d Which type has least empty space between the cans? _____

Extension

FM 1   Here is a can of baked beans. You have been asked
to design a label for the can.

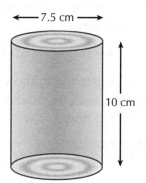

7.5 cm

10 cm

a What is the circumference of the can? _____

Hint: use the graph in exercise 13B.

b The label will be a rectangle. What size will it be?

_____

checklist

☐ I can draw circles and use vocabulary connected with them.

☐ I can use the connection between the diameter and the circumference of
a circle.

☐ I can handle circles in realistic situations.

The strength of the signal from a television transmitter depends on how far you are from the transmitter.

There are two transmitters 60 km apart.

Produce an illustration to show the distances from each transmitter to places in the surrounding area.

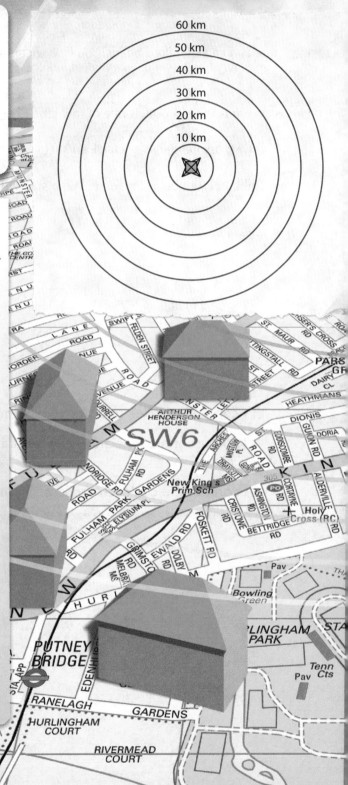

60 km
50 km
40 km
30 km
20 km
10 km

Task A

1 Mark two transmitters, A and B, 60 km apart, on a separate sheet of plain paper. Use a scale of 1 cm to 10 km.

2 Draw two sets of concentric circles, like the circle in the diagram above. Remember to use a scale of 1 cm to 1 km.

   One set will be centred on transmitter A and the other on transmitter B.

3 It will be useful to see which of the two transmitters is nearer to any particular place. Do it by working through these questions.

   a There is one point 30 km from both A and B. Mark it with a cross.

   b There are two points 40 km from A and from B. Mark them both with a cross.

   c Mark with crosses points which are:
      - 50 km from A and B
      - 60 km from A and B
      - 70 km from A and B

4 Join your crosses with a line.

   a What can you say about the line you have drawn?

   b Where are the places which are nearer to transmitter A than they are to transmitter B?

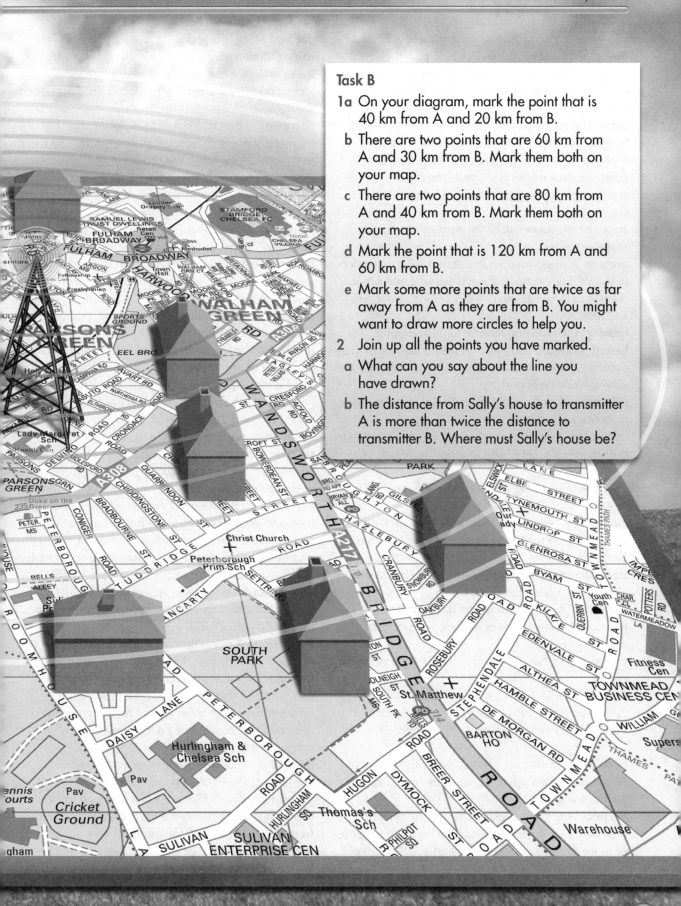

Task B

1a On your diagram, mark the point that is 40 km from A and 20 km from B.

  b There are two points that are 60 km from A and 30 km from B. Mark them both on your map.

  c There are two points that are 80 km from A and 40 km from B. Mark them both on your map.

  d Mark the point that is 120 km from A and 60 km from B.

  e Mark some more points that are twice as far away from A as they are from B. You might want to draw more circles to help you.

2 Join up all the points you have marked.

  a What can you say about the line you have drawn?

  b The distance from Sally's house to transmitter A is more than twice the distance to transmitter B. Where must Sally's house be?

Glossary

add (*add* is a verb; *addition* is the noun) A basic operation of arithmetic, shown by a plus (+) sign. To add, or addition, is the process of combining two or more values to find their total value. For example, 2 + 3 = 5.

angle The space, usually measured in degrees (°), between two straight lines that have a common endpoint (intersecting lines). The amount of turn needed to move from one line to the other.

arc A curve forming part of the circumference of a circle.

area The measurement of the amount of space a shape occupies.

average A single number that stands for a collection of values. For example, the average of 2 and 6 is 4. (Reason: 2 + 6 = 8, and 8 ÷ 2 = 4) (See also *mode* and *median*.)

bearing The direction relative to a fixed point.

biased (*biased* is an adjective; *bias* is the noun). Bias prevents something from being fair. For example, a survey could be biased.

calculator An electronic device used for working out mathematical equations.

centimetre cube A centimetre cube (cm^3) is equal to the volume of a cube with all sides the length of 1 cm.

chord A line joining two points on the circumference of a circle.

circle A curved line surrounding one central point. Every point on the line is equal distance from the centre point.

circumference The outline of a circle. The distance all the way around this outline.

clockwise Turning in the same direction as the movement of the hands of a clock. (Opposite of anticlockwise.)

concentric circles Circles that have the same centre point.

cube 1. A solid with six identical square faces. 2. The result of raising a number to the power of three. For example, 'two cubed' is written: 2^3, which is 2 × 2 × 2 = 8.

cuboid A box-shaped, solid object with faces that are all rectangles. It has six flat sides and all angles are right angles.

decimal Any number using base 10 for the number system. It usually refers to a number written with one or more decimal places. For example, $0.1 = \frac{1}{10}$, or $0.01 = \frac{1}{100}$.

decimal place Every digit in a number has a place value (hundreds, tens, ones, etc.). The places after (to the right of) the decimal point have place values of tenths, hundredths, etc. These place values are called the decimal places. (See *decimal*.)

decrease To become less or to make smaller. For example, there is a decrease in the amount of water in the urn as one lets it out.

diameter A straight line across a circle, from circumference to circumference and passing through the centre. It is the longest chord of a circle and two radii long. (See also *radius*.)

direction The way something is facing or pointing. Direction can be described using the compass points (north, south, south-east, etc.) or using bearings (the clockwise angle turned from facing north).

distance The separation (usually along a straight line) of two points. Can be referred to as length.

divide (*divide* is a verb; *division* is the noun) A basic operation of arithmetic, shown by a division (÷) sign. To split into equal groups or parts, or to 'share fairly'. For example, how can 3 friends share 6 slices of pizza? (6 ÷ 3 = 2 slices each)

equation A number sentence in which one side is equal to the other. An equation always contains an equals sign (=). For example, 9 + 4 = 8 + 5.

exchange rate Also referred to as 'rate of exchange'. Each country has a unit of currency. When one travels to another country one buys money at the current exchange rate, which is the ratio at which the unit of the currency can be exchanged. For example, during early 2010, the exchange rate for 1 GBP (Great British pound) was approximately ZAR12 (South African rand). In other words, for every pound, one could get 12 rand.

expression A collection of symbols representing a number. For example, 2 × 9.

formula (plural: formulae) An equation (numbers and symbols) that shows you how to work out a measurement from other known measurements. For example, the formula for finding the area of a rectangle is Length × Width (or *lw*).

fraction A fraction means 'part of something'. For example, $\frac{1}{5}$. The whole amount is divided into equal parts (in this case 5). A fraction has a number on top (numerator) and a number at the bottom (denominator).

frequency How often something occurs during a period of time. For example, the frequency of her heartbeat was 62 beats per minute.

increase To become more or to make larger. For example, the increase in the amount of rain since last year was 20 mm. This means we had 20 mm more rain this year than last year.

kilometres per hour (abbreviation: km/h) The number of kilometres travelled in one hour. For example, the man drove the car at 70 km/h.

litre (abbreviation: *l*) A metric measure of volume or capacity. 1 litre = 1000 millilitres = 1000 cubic centimetres.

mean The average of a group of numbers, obtained by adding them together and then dividing by the number of numbers. For example, the mean of 4, 8 and 9 is: $4 + 8 + 9 = 21$. 21 divided by 3 (the number of numbers) is 7. So the mean is 7.

median The middle value of a sample of data that is arranged in order. For example, you are asked to find the median of the sample 3, 2, 6, 2, 2, 3, 7, 4. Arrange it in order, as follows 2, 2, 2, 3, 3, 4, 6, 7. The median is the fourth value: 3.

miles per hour (abbreviation: mph) The number of miles travelled in one hour. For example, the woman's biking speed was 50 mph.

mixed number A number which is written as a whole number and a fraction. For example, $1\frac{3}{4}$ for 1.75.

mode The value that occurs most often in a sample. For example, the mode of the sample 2, 2, 3, 3, 3, 3, 4, 5, 5, is: 3.

multiply (*multiply* is a verb; *multiplication* is the noun) A basic operation of arithmetic, shown by a multiplication (×) sign. Multiplication is associated with repeated addition. For example, $3 \times 9 = 9 + 9 + 9 = 27$.

net The shape obtained when a 3-D shape is folded out flat to form a flat surface.

pattern Things arranged according to a rule or rules. For example, the pattern in the numbers 2, 10, 18, 26, 34 is: Start at 2 and add 8 every time. Tiles can also be arranged in a pattern.

perimeter The distance around the outside edge of a shape.

per hour In one hour. For example, he cycled at 20 miles per hour (20 mph). So the distance covered in one hour would be 20 miles.

percentage A number written as a fraction with 100 parts. Instead of writing $\overline{100}$ we use the symbol %. So $\frac{50}{100}$ is written as 50%.

perpendicular At right angles (90º). A line or a flat surface can also be perpendicular to another flat surface.

pie chart A chart that represents data as slices of a whole 'pie' or circle. The circle is divided into sections. The number of degrees in the angle at the centre of each section represents the frequency. (See also *frequency*.)

proportion Often used in maps drawn to scale. For example, 1 : 300 000. Also, when the ratio of the first two numbers is equal to the ratio of the next two numbers, we can say it is proportional. For example, $4 : 5 = 8 : 10$ or $\frac{4}{5} = \frac{8}{10}$. (See also *ratio*.)

questionnaire A list of questions distributed to people so that statistical information can be collected.

radius (plural: radii) The distance from the centre of a circle to its circumference (outline).

range The difference between the largest and smallest values of the data in a given set.

ratio The ratio of A to B is a number found by dividing A by B. It is written as A : B. For example, the ratio of 1 m to 1 cm is written as 1 m : 1 cm = 100 : 1. Notice that the two quantities must both be in the same units if they are to be compared.

rectangle A four-sided shape in which all the interior angles are 90°. The opposite sides are of equal length.

rounding To approximate a number so that it is accurate enough for a specific purpose. The number may be slightly reduced or increased. For example, 368 rounded to the nearest 10 = 370.

sector A region of a circle, like a slice of a pie, bounded by an arc and two radii.

sequence An ordered set of numbers that follow a rule to give the next term. For example, 3, 9, 27, 81, 243 … is a sequence, as each number is 3 times the number before it.

solution The result of, or answer to, solving a mathematical problem. Solutions are often given in equation form.

solve To find the answer to a mathematical problem. Finding the value or values of a variable *x*, which satisfy the given equation.

speed How fast something moves.

square A shape with four equal sides and all the interior angles equal to 90°.

subtract (*subtract* is a verb; *subtraction* is the noun) A basic operation of arithmetic, shown by a minus (–) sign. Subtraction is the difference between two numbers. For example, $25 – 12 = 13$. (See also *difference*.)

surface area The area of the surface of a 3-D shape, such as a cube. The area of a net will be the same as the surface area of the shape. (See also *net*.)

survey A questionnaire or interview held to find data for statistical analysis

tangent A line that just touches the circumference of a circle at one point without crossing it. Lines, curves, flat surfaces and curved surfaces can all touch in this way to form tangents.

total The whole amount; or the result of adding numbers together. For example, 3 + 4 + 6 + 9 = 22.

triangle A three-sided shape. The interior angles add up to 180°. Triangles may be classified as:
1. scalene: no sides of the triangle are equal in length (and no angles are equal).
2. equilateral: all the sides of the triangles are equal in length (and all the angles are equal).
3. isosceles: two of the sides of the triangle are equal in length (and two angles are equal).
4. A right-angled triangle has an interior angle equal to 90°.

value The result of a calculation. For example, 6 × 7 gives the value of 42. Or, how much something is worth.

volume The amount of space enclosed by a 3-D shape. The amount of substance that fills a container.

whole number Numbers that are not negative, or decimals or fractions. For example, 0, 1, 2, 3, 4 … 49, 580, etc.

Notes

William Collins' dream of knowledge for all began with the publication of his first book in 1819. A self-educated mill worker, he not only enriched millions of lives, but also founded a flourishing publishing house. Today, staying true to this spirit, Collins books are packed with inspiration, innovation and practical expertise. They place you at the centre of a world of possibility and give you exactly what you need to explore it.

Collins. Freedom to teach.

Published by Collins
An imprint of HarperCollinsPublishers
77–85 Fulham Palace Road
Hammersmith
London
W6 8JB

Browse the complete Collins catalogue at
www.collinseducation.com

10 9 8 7 6 5 4 3 2 1
ISBN-13 978-0-00-734025-5

Chris Pearce asserts his moral rights to be identified as the author of this work

British Library Cataloguing in Publication Data
A Catalogue record for this publication is available from the British Library

Commissioned by Priya Govindan
Project managed by Aimée Walker
Edited and proofread by Brian Asbury and Marian Bond
Answer check by Marian Bond
Cover design by Angela English
Concept design by Nigel Jordan
Illustrations by Kathy Baxendale and Gray Publishing
Design and typesetting by Linda Miles,
Lodestone Publishing
Functional maths and problem-solving pages designed and illustrated by Jerry Fowler and edited and proofread by Rachel Faulkner
Glossary by Gudrun Kaiser
Production by Leonie Kellman
Printed and bound by L.E.G.O. S.p.A. Italy

Acknowledgements
The publishers have sought permission from Edexcel to reproduce questions from past GCSE Mathematics papers.

The publishers wish to thank the following for permission to reproduce photographs. Every effort has been made to trace copyright holders and to obtain their permission for the use of copyright material. The publishers will gladly receive any information enabling them to rectify any error or omission at the first opportunity.

p.14 sonicken/iStockphoto; pp. 16–17 © kavu/iStockphoto; pp. 28–29 © nikitje/iStockphoto, © Jerry Fowler; pp. 44–45 © Soundsnaps/Dreamstime.com, © Daniela Spyropoulou/Dreamstime.com, © Mikael Damkier/Dreamstime.com; pp. 58–59 © Elena Elisseeva/Dreamstime.com, © Redeyed/Dreamstime.com,© Jerry Fowler; pp. 70–71 © Mrloz/Dreamstime.com; pp. 82–83 © Mehmet Dilsiz/Dreamstime.com, © http://en.wikipedia.org/wiki/File:Orange_and_T.Mobile_shops_in_Leeds.JPGMtaylor848; pp. 96–97 © Jerry Fowler, © Jaggat .../Dreamstime.com, © Alexshu/Dreamstime.com; pp. 110–111 © Jerry Fowler, © Stoke City FC, © Lario Tus/Dreamstime.com, © Richard Thomas/Dreamstime.com, Paul Ellis/gettyimages.co.uk; pp. 122–123 © Monika Adamczyk/Dreamstime.com, © Geraldine Rychter/Dreamstime.com, © Margaryta Vakhterova/Dreamstime.com, © Elena Schweitzer/Dreamstime.com, © Baloncici/Dreamstime.com, © Ildar Akhmerov/Dreamstime.com, © Olga Nayashkova/Dreamstime.com, © Darren Fisher/Dreamstime.com, © Lana Langlois/Dreamstime.com, © Lepas/Dreamstime.com, © Tund/Dreamstime.com, © Roman Ivaschenko/Dreamstime.com, © Monika3stepsahead/Dreamstime.com, © YinYang/iStockphoto.com, © Virginia Hamrick/iStockphoto, © Robynmac/Dreamstime.com, © Sabina-s/Dreamstime.com, © Yasonya/Dreamstime.com, © Yasonya/Dreamstime.com, © Rcmathiraj/Dreamstime.com, © Linda & Colin McKie/iStockphoto, © Kieran Wills/iStockphoto, © ALEAIMAGE/iStockphoto, © Julien Grondin/iStockphoto, © Norman Chan/iStockphoto, © Jerry Fowler; pp. 134–135 © Cool(r)/Dreamstime.com, © Catherine Yeulet/iStockphoto.com, © digitalskillet//iStockphoto, © Yuri Arcurs/Dreamstime.com; pp. 146–147 © Daboost/Dreamstime.com, © David Gaylor/Dreamstime.com, © Saniphoto/Dreamstime.com; pp. 158–159 © Kristian Sekulic/Dreamstime.com, © South12th/Dreamstime.com, © Mackon/Dreamstime.com, © Danny Smythe/Dreamstime.com, © Jerry Fowler; pp. 170–171 © Daniel Gale/Dreamstime.com, © Jerry Fowler, © Collins Bartholomew Ltd 2009.

With thanks to Jan Parry (Secondary Mathematics Consultant, Leicester), Peter Thompson and Annie Sutton (The Angmering School), and Steve Nutting (Oasis Academy, Shirley Park).

Answers

Chapter 1 Using a calculator

Exercise 1A

1 84

2 816

3 15

4 £217

5 17 weeks

6 The answer is always 1.

7 **a** 1440   **b** 8760

Extension

1 36×54

2 7, 11 and 13

3 Carlos has 263 euros and Juan has 213.

Exercise 1B

1 **a** $\frac{2}{3}$ **b** $\frac{3}{4}$ **c** $\frac{3}{5}$ **d** $\frac{7}{8}$

2 $\frac{3}{6} = \frac{5}{10}; \frac{4}{6} = \frac{12}{18}; \frac{9}{27} = \frac{7}{21}$

3 Possible answers are $\frac{7}{10}, \frac{14}{20}, \frac{21}{30}, \frac{35}{50}$ and so on.

4 **a** $\frac{5}{6}$ **b** $\frac{5}{8}$ **c** $\frac{7}{12}$ **d** $\frac{7}{8}$

   e $\frac{2}{3}$ **f** $\frac{5}{6}$

5 There are lots of possible answers, including $\frac{1}{3} + \frac{1}{6}$ or $\frac{1}{8} + \frac{3}{8}$.

6 **a** $1\frac{1}{4}$ **b** $2\frac{1}{3}$ **c** $2\frac{3}{4}$ **d** $5\frac{3}{4}$

   e $4\frac{1}{3}$ **f** $2\frac{5}{6}$

7 **a** $1\frac{1}{4}$ **b** $1\frac{1}{6}$ **c** $1\frac{3}{8}$ **d** $1\frac{3}{8}$

   e $1\frac{1}{4}$ **f** $1\frac{3}{4}$

8 **a** The sector from 12 to 3 is $\frac{1}{4}$.

   The sector from 8 to 12 is $\frac{1}{3}$.

   The other sector is $\frac{5}{12}$. Together they make a whole clock face.

9 **a** $\frac{2}{3}$ **b** $\frac{5}{8}$ **c** $\frac{1}{4}$ **d** $\frac{3}{8}$

   e $1\frac{1}{4}$ **f** $1\frac{1}{3}$

10 Top row: $\frac{1}{2}, \frac{7}{12}, \frac{3}{4}, 1$;

   second row: $\frac{7}{12}, \frac{2}{3}, \frac{5}{6}, 1\frac{1}{12}$;

   third row: $\frac{3}{4}, \frac{5}{6}, 1, 1\frac{1}{4}$;

   fourth row: $1, 1\frac{1}{12}, 1\frac{1}{4}, 1\frac{1}{2}$

Extension

1 Because the answer is positive.

2 $\frac{2}{3}$ is bigger because $\frac{2}{3} - \frac{5}{8}$ is positive.

3 **a** $4\frac{1}{4}$ **b** $1\frac{3}{4}$ **c** $2\frac{3}{4}$

Exercise 1C

1 **a** 58 465   **b** 3205

2 Yes. The average is 65.5.

3 **a** £572   **b** £1368   **c** £162

4 £353

5 £796

6 Option B is £465 cheaper.

7 £0.96

8 £11.36, £22.99, £18, Total £91.82

Extension

1   Sale prices are £38, £118 and £312.

2   £342

Functional Maths

Task A

1   28

2   28

3   39

4   46

Task B

12 red beads and 12 blue beads.

Task C

Student's own design and list.

Task D

Student's own costing.

Chapter 2 Constructions

Exercise 2A

1   **a** 6.5 cm **b** 8.4 cm **c** 11.8 cm

2   9.5 cm, 6.4 cm, 35°

3   Student's own drawing. Other angles should be 30° and 60°.

Extension

1   **a** 8.3 cm **b** 11.3 cm **c** 6.2 cm

2   Student's own drawings.
Third angles should be:
a 75° **b** 67° **c** 65° **d** 110°
e 42° **f** 60°

3   **a i** Isosceles   **ii** Both 6.7 cm
    b i Equilateral   **ii** 7.5 cm
       iii Student's own check

4   Student's own drawings.

5   Student's own check.

6   **a** Student's own drawing.
    b It is impossible because 4 + 6 is less than 11
    c Student's own drawing.

Exercise 2B

1   **a** 105°   **b** 150°

2   Hill 075°, mosque 155°, wood 217°, church 325°

3   **a** 080°   **b** 260°

Extension

1   **a** 130°   **b** 300 km

2   **a** 25 miles   **b** 030°
    c Student's own drawing.
    d Student's own drawing.

Exercise 2C

1   Clockwise from north, 000°, 045°, 090°, 135°, 180°, 225°, 270°, and 315°

2   Student's own drawing.

3   **a** 075°   **b** 650 km **c** 255°

4   **a**

	Bearing	Distance
Glasgow to turn	165°	170 miles
turn to Manchester	100°	40 miles

    b To avoid planes travelling in the opposite direction from Manchester to Glasgow.

Extension

1   Student's own drawing.

Problem Solving

Student's own activity.

Chapter 3 Calculating with numbers

Exercise 3A

1 **b** 800   **c** 1500   **d** 2400

2 **a** 441   **b** 44 100

3 The missing numbers are 42, 420 and 42 000

4

28	280
280	2800

5 **a** 276   **b** 1008   **c** 1148   **d** 1425

6 **a** 1431   **b** 53   **c** 27

7 $6351 \div 87 = 73$ and $6351 \div 73 = 87$

8 **a** 12   **b** 13   **c** 32   **d** 28

Extension

1 47×63 is larger. The difference is 80.

2 32

Exercise 3B

1 **a** 43   **b** 52   **c** 2   **d** 4
    e 12   **f** 15   **g** 3   **h** 81
    i 99   **j** 67   **k** 13   **l** 9

2 **b** 6.8   **c** 8.9   **d** 14.5   **e** 11.6
    f 58.5   **g** 8.6   **h** 3.8

3 **a** 4.66   **b** 3.34   **c** 8.88
    d 11.32   **e** 32.90   **f** 14.32

4 £28.57

5 **a** 7.6   **b** 16.6   **c** 13.1   **d** 47.6

6 2.86

Extension

1 Give each person £15.38 and there will be 6p left over.

Exercise 3C

1 **a** 5.74   **b** 13.6   **c** 3.7   **d** 3.7

2 **a** 8.1   **b** 14.44   **c** 14   **d** 75.6

3 **a** 1.9   **b** 1.36   **c** 0.53   **d** 3.72

4 £9.60

5 £1.90

Extension

1 £3.75

2 **a** 94.5   **b** 94.5   **c** 9.45

3 **a** 1134   **b** 113.4

4 **a** 37   **b** 3.7

Exercise 3D

1 **a** £1.80   **b** £1.75   **c** 40p

2 **a** £4.50   **b** £5.00   **c** £9.20

3 **a** £15.98   **b** £4.02

4 **a** 6   **b** £507.15

5 83p

6 £17.50

7 **a** £15.50   **b** £29.90

8 **a** £248   **b** £9.10

Extension

1 19.8 m

2 Mobilz is £15.90 cheaper.

Functional Maths

Task A

1 Cheapest: Salad, Veal Escalope, Fruit Salad: 19.35 Euros.
Most Expensive: Salmon Mousse, Pork Fillet, Creme Brûlée: 27.05 Euros.

2 Angie: 23.20 Euros
Ken: 22.55 Euros

3 51.45 Euros

4 10% of bill is 5.145 Euros, round up to 5.15 Euros.

5 They paid 56.60 Euros, including the tip.

6 56.60 × 0.91 = 51.506, round up to £51.51.

Task B

Student's own choice.

Chapter 4 Pie charts and surveys

Exercise 4A

1 blue 20, red 10, green 5, purple 5

2 Student's own pie chart.

3 Ash 70°, 7; beech 90°, 9; other 140°, 14

4 12° for each vote; 108°, 120°, 48°, 84°

5 **a** $\frac{1}{4}$ **b** 60

Extension

1 Student's own pie chart.

2 **a** True **b** Cannot tell
   c Cannot tell **d** False
   e True **f** False **g** Cannot tell
   h Cannot tell **i** Cannot tell

3 60°, 120°, 108°; student's own drawing.

Exercise 4B

1 **a** Student's own suggestions.
   b Then everyone can fill one box.
   c Answers may be different on different days.

2 **a** Student's own suggestions.
   b Student's own suggestions.

3 Possible answers: 1 hour is in two boxes; no box for over 6 hours; it does not specify when, for example yesterday.

4 **a** Possible answers: no box for none; no time period is given.
   b One reason is that they might all be the same age.

Extension

1 **a** Possible reasons are: no girls asked; all are a similar age.
   b Student's own suggestion.

Exercise 4C

1 **a** One third of the chart is coloured blue for 'no'.
   b No **c** 9
   d Student's own suggestion.
   e It does not matter if the class sizes are different.

2 **a** There are other possibilities besides 'Always' and 'Never'.
   b Student's own suggestions.
   c Student's own ideas.

3 **a** It is easy to analyse the results.
   b Student's own suggestions.

Extension

1 **a** and **b** Student's own suggestions.
   c It is a good way to show proportions.
   d Many people are at work on Friday mornings; children will be at school unless it is a holiday.

2 Student's own ideas.

Functional Maths

1 **a** Probably 0–19 **b** 20–39
   c 60 and over
   d No. You cannot find numbers from a pie chart.

2 **a** 20–39 **b** about 25%
   c about 15%

3 **a** North East **b** London
   c London

4 **a** Birmingham, because about 30% of the population are under 20 years old. In Torbay the proportion is only about 20%.
   b Torbay, because about 30% of the residents are 60 and over. The figure for Birmingham is only about 20%.

c Student's own comments.

d Student's own suggestions. Some possible factors might be that retired people move to Torbay and that there are more job opportunities in Birmingham.

Chapter 5 Percentages
Exercise 5A

1 30%

2 63% and 90%

3 a $\frac{1}{4}$ and $\frac{3}{4}$ b 25% and 75%

4 0.45, 30%, 70%, 75%, 15%

5 50% = $\frac{1}{2}$, 20% = $\frac{1}{5}$, 30% = $\frac{3}{10}$

6 $\frac{1}{4}$, $\frac{3}{4}$, $\frac{1}{5}$, $\frac{1}{10}$, $\frac{9}{10}$

7 The largest is $\frac{7}{8}$ (= 87.5%); $\frac{4}{5}$ is only 80%

8 35%

9 8%, $\frac{3}{10}$, 0.35, 0.63, 70%, $\frac{4}{5}$

Extension

1 a 75% b 60% c 40% d 55%

2 a $\frac{2}{5}$ b 0.98   c 7 500 000
   d 25%   e 60%

Exercise 5B

1 $\frac{1}{2}$ and 50%, $\frac{1}{4}$ and 25%, $\frac{3}{4}$ and 75%,

   $\frac{1}{10}$ and 10%

2 b £36 c £60 d £76 e £6.48
   f £7.35

3

£9	£18	£27
£16	£32	£48
£30	£60	£90

4 a 13 kg   b 20 m
   c 36 cars   d 450 drivers

5 a 600 vehicles   b 150 tonnes
   c £113.68

6 a £50.40
   b For example, 24% of £420 is £100.80 or 3% of £420 is £12.60

7 a 44% b 476 c 374

8

42%	1512
23%	828
19%	684
16%	576

9 £960

Extension

1 £453.60

2 £108

3 50%

4 History. He got 84%, whereas in geography he got 80%.

Exercise 5C

1 a $\frac{17}{20}$ b 85%

2 90%

3 a 72%, 70%, 80%, 67%
   b Engineering

4 a 75 grams   b 375 grams

5 360 ml

6 276 grams

7 They are both £12.

8 a 50% b 40% c 60%

Extension

1 Yes; 25% of 4 is 1, so 5 is 25% extra.

2 a 20%   b 26%
   c There are far more people in the UK than just in London, so the number of young adults will be greater even if the percentage is less.

d Greater

e One possible reason is that young adults move to London to work and then leave when they get older.

Functional Maths

Task A

1

	Module 1	Module 2	Module 3
Aziz	82.5%	70%	68%
Barry	70%	55%	74%
Claire	75%	82.5%	80%
Donna	67.5%	55%	64%
Emily	90%	60%	53.3%
Franz	70%	45%	58%

2 Only Franz did not pass all three modules.

Task B

1 Student's own answer.

2 Claire had the most consistent results because the graph shows that her percentages for each module were the most similar.

Task C

1

	Total mark out of 350	Overall percentage
Aziz	252	72%
Barry	233	66.6%
Claire	279	79.7%
Donna	216	61.7%
Emily	224	58.3%
Franz	197	56.3%

2 Claire will be awarded a distinction.

Chapter 6 Using algebra

Exercise 6A

1 **a** 19 **b** 8 **c** 32

2 **b** $R + 4$ **c** $2R$ **d** $\frac{1}{2}R$ or $R \div 2$

3 **a** Fatima is seven years older than Jack.
b Will is two years younger than Jack.
c Aya is three times Jack's age.

d Lachan is half Jack's age.

4 $20x$

5 **a** 15 **b** 1 **c** 3
d −2 **e** 12 **f** 30

6 **a** 32 **b** 8 **c** 58
d 5 **e** 8 **f** 41

Extension

1 **a** You have to add the lengths of the 4 sides: $L + L + L + L = 4L$
b $6L$

2 **a** 30 **b** 30
c Because adding two numbers and trebling the total is the same as trebling each one and adding the answers.

3 **a** A is $10a + 4b$; B is $6A + 10B$; C is $6a + 8b$
b Correct shape

Exercise 6B

1 **a** 12 m **b** 18 m

2 **a** £50 **b** £85

3 **a** 12 cm **b** 27 m

4 **a** Free **b** £1 **c** £5

5 **a** £50 **b** £90

6 **a** 100 minutes **b** 80 minutes
c 92 minutes

Extension

1 40 people

2 $3x + 2y$

Exercise 6C

1 **a** 105 minutes
b

	1 kg	1.5 kg	2 kg	2.5 kg
Rare	55	75	95	115
Medium rare	70	90	110	130
Well done	85	105	125	145

c Cooking time in minutes =
weight in kg × 40 + 45

2 **a** Length of visit in hours × 24 + 30
b £66   **c** 3 hours
d This is a possible table.

Length of visit in hours	1	1.5	2	2.5
Cost in £	54	66	78	90

Extension

1 **a** £130
b Cost in pounds =
number of days × 10 + 80

Functional Maths

1 **SuperDeal A**

Texts in a month	0	50	100	150	200	250	300	350	400
Cost in pounds	24.47	24.47	24.47	24.47	30.47	36.47	42.47	48.47	54.47

SuperDeal B

Texts in a month	0	50	100	150	200	250	300	350	400
Cost in pounds	29.36	29.36	29.36	29.36	29.36	35.36	41.36	47.36	53.36

SuperDeal C

Texts in a month	0	50	100	150	200	250	300	350	400
Cost in pounds	34.25	34.25	34.25	34.25	34.25	34.25	34.25	34.25	37.25

2 If she sends more than 250 texts a month then deal C is best. If she sends less than 250 texts a month then B or A might be better.

3 If he makes up to 150 minutes of calls, Deal A will be best; if he makes between 150 and 300 minutes of calls, Deal B will be best; if he makes more than 300 minute of calls, Deal C will be best.

4 Student's own choice

Chapter 7 Averages

Exercise 7A

1 **a** 20   **b** indigo   **c** red

2 **a** Football, rugby, tennis and cricket equal, hockey

b Football **c** Rugby

3 **a** 33 mph **b** 14 mph **c** 109

4 **a** 25   **b** 20   **c** 15

5 **a** £8.72   **b** £3.71   **c** £9.13
d £3.71 (the same)

Extension

1 **a** 18   **b** 3 years **c** 17

2 **a** 42   **b** 25   **c** 30

3 7 minutes

Exercise 7B

1 6.4 minutes

2 10.6

3 **a** 19   **b** 6

4   **a** 20   **b** 3.05   **c** 3   **d** 3
  e Could be mode, median or mean.

5   **a** Both are 75 cm
  b 81.8 cm and 83 cm
  c Boys, mean is larger
  d 20 cm   **e** 21 cm

6   **a** Blonde   **b** Becky   **c** 7

Extension

1   B, because 2250 ÷ 50 = 45

2   **a** 12 minutes   **b** 52 minutes
  c 7 minutes   **d** By 5 minutes
  e 7 minutes   **f** 6.5 minutes
  g By 0.5 minutes

Exercise 7C

1   **a** 1.78 goals and 1.22 goals
  b 1 goal and 1 goal
  c Norwich has a slightly higher mean but they both have the same median.

2   **a** 42.95   **b** 42   **c** 38
  d Yes; if he used this median time.
  e 34
  f Journeys were longer in May but there was less variation in the times.

3   **a** Klara, lowest median
  b Louise, smallest range

4   **a** Office Administrator
  b IT Project Manager
  c Either '£21 319 or more' or '£21 319 or less' is correct.

5   **a** 16°F   **b** 75.75°F   **c** 76°F
  d Either the mean or the median because both are averages.

Extension

1   30.5

2   The girls are heavier on average. There is more variation in the boys' weights.

Problem Solving

Task A

1   Championship: 27

League 1:   26
League 2:   30

2   Championship: 2.25
  League 1:   2.16
  League 2:   2.5

3   They are all quite similar, apart from the Premier League, which is larger than the other three.

Task B

The mode is 2 for the Championship, League 1 and League 2, but there is no mode for the Premier League.

Task C

Student's own answer.

Chapter 8 Area and perimeter

Exercise 8A

1   **a** 18   **b** 28

2   **a** 120m   **b** 170 m   **c** 150 m

3   10 cm

4   There are many possibilities: 4 cm, 5 cm, 5 cm and 6 cm is one.

5   **a** 16 cm   **b** 18 m   **c** 36 mm

6   20 m

Extension

1   Triangle 12 cm, square 9 cm

2   160 cm

Exercise 8B

1   **a** 20   **b** 22

2   31 km^2 to 37 km^2

3   **a** 26 cm   **b** 30 cm^2

4   **a** 15 cm^2 **b** 20 m^2 **c** 17 mm^2

5   **a** 60 cm   **b** 200 cm^2

6   **a** 72 m^2 and 20 m^2 **b** 92 m^2

Extension

1 124 m^2

2 **a** 40 cm^2 **b** 20 cm^2

3 **a** 9 cm^2 **b** 28 cm

Exercise 8C

1 **a** 210 feet
b 2106 square feet.

2 **a** 228 feet
b 2808 square feet.

3 No. 2808 is not double 2106.

4 **a** Singles perimeter is 122 feet and area is 748 square feet.
b Doubles perimeter is 128 feet and area is 880 square feet.

5 **a** 320 yards
b 6000 square yards

6 **a** The area
b Perimeter = 17.2 m, area = 17.85 m^2
c To fit an edging border is one reason.

7 **a** Area = 24 m^2; 24 × £8.49 = £203.76
b Perimeter is 20 m, so 8 pieces are needed. £20 × 8 = £160
c No, you still need 8 pieces because doors are generally less than 1 metre wide and the skirting board is sold in lengths of 2.5 metres.

Extension

1 Along the 3.3 m side you need 7 tiles.
Along the 4.8 m side you need 10 tiles.
7 × 10 = 70
70 × £3.49 = £244.30

Functional Maths

Task A

1 The maximum area of a senior pitch is 10 800 m^2.
The maximum perimeter of a senior pitch is 420 m.

2 **a** The minimum size for a senior pitch is 90 m long and 45.5 m wide.
b The minimum area of a senior pitch is 4095 m^2.
The minimum perimeter of a senior pitch is 271 m.

3 There is a big difference.
The maximum-sized pitch is more than twice the area of the minimum one.

Task B

1 Student's own scale drawings.

2 The table below shows the areas and perimeters of the pitches (rounded to the nearest whole unit):

Pitch	Maximum		Minimum	
	Area (m^2)	Perimeter (m)	Area (m^2)	Perimeter (m)
Seniors	10 800	420	4095	271
Under 16	6438	329	3745	256
Under 14	5096	294	3312	237
Under 12	4163	266	2867	221

3 Student's own comparisons.

4 Student's own recommendation.

Chapter 9 Ratio and proportion

Exercise 9A

1 16

2 **a** 7 : 4   **b** 4 : 7

3 2 : 1

4 **a** 3   **b** 3

5 **b** 3 : 1   **c** 4 : 1   **d** 3 : 4
      e 3 : 2   **f** 2 : 5   **g** 2 : 3

6 **a** 15   **b** 20   **c** $\frac{1}{4}$

7 **a** 1 : 10   **b** 4 : 1

8 **a** true   **b** false   **c** true   **d** true

9 **a** 2 : 1   **b** $\frac{2}{3}$

Extension

1 **a** tulips 5, daffodils 15   **b** $\frac{1}{4}$

2 **a** 2 : 1   **b** $\frac{2}{3}$

3 $\frac{2}{5}$

4 62

Exercise 9B

1 **a** 12 miles   **b** 24 miles
      c 60 miles

2 **a** 50 miles   **b** 100 miles
      c 150 miles

3 80 miles

4

Time (hours)	0.5	1	2	3	4
Distance (miles)	15	30	60	90	120

5 **a** 34 cm   **b** 68 cm   **c** 170 cm

6 12 km/h

7 **a** 7 mph   **b** 15 mph   **c** 12 mph

8 **a** 12   **b** 5

9 **a** 70 miles   **b** 210 miles
      c 35 miles   **d** 105 miles

10 8 hours

11 60 km/h

12 **a** 24   **b** 48   **c** 12   **d** 6

Extension

1 **a** going 15 mph; coming back 10 mph
      b 12 mph

2 18 km/h

Exercise 9C

1 **a** 3 : 1   **b** 6 : 1   **c** 5 : 1
      d 3 : 2 or 1.5 : 1

2 butter 180, chocolate 240, flour 60,
      cocoa 40, sugar 300, eggs 4

3 12

4 270 g

5 **a** 14.50   **b** 290   **c** £344.83

6 **a** 16   **b** 32   **c** 15
      d 80, 60, 160, 320, 250
      e Yes, 1 mile = 1.6 km   **f** 40 000 km

Extension

1 **a** 94p   **b** 85p   **c** Large

2 200 ml – £1.20 per 100 ml as opposed
      to £1.33 per 100 ml

3 600 g – price per 100 g is only 79p
      400 g is 85p per 100 g

Functional Maths

Starter:
325 g potatoes
20 g plain flour
65 g peas
65 g carrots
1 small onion
half–1 red chilli (depending on how hot you
   like it)
1 clove of garlic

$\frac{1}{2}$ teaspoon of cinnamon
$\frac{1}{2}$ teaspoon of cumin
Juice of $\frac{1}{2}$ of a small lime
1 tablespoon of chopped coriander
Salt and oil

Main
600 g aubergines
1 large onion
300 g minced lamb
2 medium eggs
Salt and pepper

Dessert
80 g plain flour
40 g wholemeal flour
1 large egg or 2 medium eggs
$\frac{1}{4}$ teaspoon of vanilla essence
$\frac{1}{2}$ teaspoon of ground cinnamon
3 small Cox's apples
4 tablespoons dry cider

Chapter 10 Equations

Exercise 10A

1   a 10   b 13   c 10   d 18
  e 45   f 25

2   a 17   b 20   c 30   d 40
  e 51   f 60

3   a 6   b 11   c 25

4   a 16   b 50   c 80   d 30
  e 24   f 80

5   45p

6   34p

7   £6.35

8   a 35   b 3   c 48   d 6
  e 27   f 40

9   a 12, 20   b 10, 30
  c 7, 6   d 10.5, 15

Extension

1   a 3   b 5   c 8

2   a −8, −5   b −20, −14
  c −9, −13   d −12, −15

Exercise 10B

1   a 15   b 7
2   a 11   b 6.7
3   a 4   b 6
4   a 6   b 18
5   a 4   b 8   c 7   d 4
  e 30
6   a 4   b 10   c 9   d 16
7   a 6   b 19   c 10

Extension

1   a −4   b −7   c −5   d 3.6
  e 2.5   f 10.5

Exercise 10C

1   $C = 8$
2   a $2C + 8 = 20$ b $C = 6$
3   Student's own story.
4   a 6   b $4N + 6 = 18$ c 3
5   a $5N − 12$ b $5N − 12 = 53$
  c 13
6   Student's own story.

Extension

1   a 68, 86, 104 and student's own numbers
  b $C = 100$ c 60 °C   d 150 °C

Functional Maths

Task A

1   20
2   Only £50 will be collected, which is £50 less than spent.
3   30

4 19

5 There will be a loss of £30.

6 About 34 tickets (17 of each).

Task B

1 34

2 He needs to sell about 40 tickets (10 adults, 10 senior citizens, 20 children).

Chapter 11 Number sequences and patterns

Exercise 11A

1 **a** 16 **b** 19 **c** 26 **d** 13 **e** 43 **f** 87

2 **a** 24, 27 **b** Add 3

3 **a** 27 **b** 52 **c** 64 **d** 26 **e** 56 **f** 24

4 **a** 32 **b** 48 **c** 5, 10, 20, 40, …

5 **a** 13332 **b** 15554 **c** 46662

6 **a** 3 **b** Subtract 4

7 **a** 19, 22 **b** Add 3

Extension

1 **a** 20 **b** 35 **c** 31

2 **a** 17, 33 **b** 25, 49

3 13, 21, 34

4 11111 × 11111 = 123454321

Exercise 11B

1 **a** OXOXOXOXO **b** 3, 5, 7, 9 **c** 11

2 **a** 3, 5, 7 **b** Shape with 9 squares **c** 11

3 **a** 4 squares joined together **b** Dots 6, 8, 10; lines 7, 10, 13 **c** 12, 16

4 **a** T-shape drawn made of 10 dots. **b** 10, 13

5 **a** 6 **b** Student's own drawing. Three extra sticks added to the pattern. **c** 12, 15

Extension

1 **a** ABCDEDCBA **b** 3 **c** 5 **d** 7 **e** 19

2 Student's own drawing.

Exercise 11C

1 2, 6, 8

2 **a** 9 metres **b** 3, 9, 12 **c** 15 metres **d** 9

3 **a** Horizontals: 3, 5, 6. Side pieces: 2, 2, 2. **b** 9

Extension

1 **a** Student's own drawing.s **b** Corner stones: 4, 4, 4. Straights: 4, 8, 10 **c** 4, 14 **d** Student's own examples.

2 **a** Student's own drawing; 6 **b** 4, 6, 8, 10, 12 **c** 22 **d** Student's own examples.

3 **a** £75.20 **b** 6

Problem Solving

Task A

a 110

b 000011

c No repeating pattern

d 001010

e No repeating pattern

f 00100011

Task B

1 **a** The sequence is 10011 and it is 5 bits long
 b 16th, 21st, 26th….
 c 11001110011100111…..
 Yes, because it has the same pattern of two 0s and three 1s.

2 **a** 1 **b** 1 **c** 1
 d The 1st, 5th, 9th, 13th, etc will be 0s and the rest will be 1s

3 Student's own answer

Task C

1 **a** 8000 **b** 8 million

2 **a** 00101100 **b** 0, 1 and 0

3 Student's own solution

4 Student's own solution

Chapter 12 Volume

Exercise 12A

1 **a** 4 cm **b** 4 cm^3 **c** 18 cm^2

2 **a** 4 cm^3 **b** 6 **c** 16 cm^2

3 Student's own answer.

4 **a** A: 6 cm^3 and 22 cm^2
 B: 6 cm^3 and 24 cm^2
 b Student's own answer.

5 **a** 12 cm **b** 5 cm^3 **c** 22 cm^2

6 **a** 24 cm **b** 15 cm^2 **c** 20 cm^3

Extension

1 **a** A: 8 cm^3 and 24 cm^2
 B: 8 cm^3 and 34 cm^2
 b Student's own answer.

2 Student's own answers

Exercise 12B

1 **a** 12 cm^3 **b** 30 cm^3

2 **a** 32 cm^3 **b** 72 cm^3 **c** 42 cm^3

3 **a** 142 cm^2
 b length = 7 cm, width = 5 cm, height = 3 cm
 c 105 cm^3

4 **a** 32 cm^2; 2(2 × 2) = 8, 4(3 × 2) = 24, 8 + 24 = 32
 b 62 cm^2; 2(2 × 3) = 12, 2(2 × 5) = 20, 2(3 × 5) = 30, 12 + 20 + 30 = 62

5 **a** 20 m^2 **b** 50 m^3

6 **a** 72 cm^3 **b** Student's own answer.

7 150

Extension

1 **a** 2 × 2 × 15 = 60
 b Student's own answers.

Exercise 12C

1 10

2 6 m^3

3 **a** 120 m^3 **b** 120 000 litres

Extension

1 **a** 210 cm^3
 b Because 220 matches can fit in a box with a volume of 210 cm^3.
 c 228 cm^2, 2(12 × 7) = 168, 2(12 × 2.5 = 60, 168 + 60 = 228
 d 179 cm^2, 12 × 7 = 84, 2(2.5 × 7) = 35, 2(2.5 × 12) = 60, 84 + 35 + 60 = 179
 e The card needs to overlap and to be joined. The tray needs to be slightly smaller than the sleeve.

2 **a** 102 m^2
 b 11 plus student's own explanations.
 c 210 m^3
 d No it does not; 15 × 11 = 165
 e £1154.30

Functional Maths

Task A

1 The volume of the large carton =
$7 \times 7.5 \times 20 = 1050$ cm^3. 1 litre =
1000 cm^3. Therefore the carton can
hold 1 litre.

2 The volume of the small carton =
$5 \times 4 \times 11 = 220$ cm^3. This is more
than 200 ml so the carton can hold
200 ml.

3 Make a net of the carton to work out
the area of the cardboard needed to
make a carton. The area of cardboard
for the large carton = 685 cm^2.
The area of cardboard to make a small
carton = 238 cm^2.
Area for large carton ÷ area for small
carton = 685 ÷ 238 = 2.88
The large carton needs less than 3 times
the amount of cardboard the small
carton requires. This shows that the
manager's theory is incorrect.

Task B

1 Student's own investigation.

2 The surface area is the amount of
transparent plastic film it will take to
enclose the six-pack.
Calculate the surface area of a few of
the arrangements to show the manager
that the different arrangements will
require different amounts of transparent
plastic film. This will show that the
manager's theory is incorrect.

Task C

Student's own recommendation. Student
should calculate the surface area of the base
of each arrangement to find the one that takes
up the smallest amount of space on the shelf.
Reasons behind the recommendations
include these points.

- Stacking is easier with larger base area
  compared to height.

- The amount of transparent plastic film
  is determined by the surface area.

- The visual impact is highest when the
  largest faces of the cartons face the
  customer when displayed on the
  shelves.

- The ease of carrying in a shopping bag
  is minimised by reducing the
  'bulkiness' of the six-pack. Minimising
  all three dimensions (width, height and
  depth) will therefore be optimum.

Chapter 13 Circles

Exercise 13A

1 **a** 3.5, 2.5, 2 cm
   b Student's own drawing.
   c 7, 5, 4, 6 cm

2 **a** Radius   **b** Tangent
   c to **f** Student's own drawing

3 **a** Diameter   **b** Radius
   c Tangent   **d** Radius
   e Chord   **f** Centre

4 Circle and chord, circle and radius,
   circle and diameter, circle and sector

5 **a** 6 cm   **b** 3 cm

6 Student's own drawing.

Extension

1 Student's own drawing.

Exercise 13B

Answers in this exercise are approximate.
Values close to these are also correct.

1 **a** 31 cm   **b** 16 mm   **c** 25 m
   d 31 km   **e** 19 mm   **f** 22 m

2 **a** 19 cm   **b** 28 m   **c** 12.5 cm

3 **a** Between 6 and 7 cm
   b Student's own drawing.
   c Hard to measure if you cannot get at
      the end of the pipe.

4   Between 4 and 5 metres

Extension

1   **a** $31\frac{3}{7}$ cm or between 31 and 32 cm.
      b It should be the same.

2   **a** 62.8 metres is two times 31.4 metres
      b Missing numbers are 15.7, 62.8 and 125.6

3   About 31 cm

4   **a** About 12 500 miles
      b About 8000 miles

Exercise 13C

1   **a** 1p 20 mm; 2p 25 mm; 5p 18 mm; 10p 24 mm; £1 22 mm; £2 28 mm
      b No, a 2p is larger than 5p and 50p is larger than £1.

2   Student's own drawing.

3   **a** square packing
      b Student's own drawing
      c Student's own drawing
      d Hexagonal

Extension

1   **a** About 24 cm
      b Width 10 cm. Length at least 24 cm and probably longer to give an overlap.

Problem Solving

Task A

1   Student's own drawing

2   Student's own drawing

3   Student's own drawing

4   **a** Every point on the line is equal distance (equidistant) from A and B.
      b All the places that fall on the same side of the line as A will be nearer to transmitter A than transmitter B.

Task B

1   Student's own drawings

2   **a** The points form a circle of radius 40 km. The centre of the circle is 80 km from A and 20 km from B.
      b Inside the circle.